PRACTICAL DATA COMM
MODEMS, NETWORKS AND

C000231268

Huly Donnelly

INDUSTRIAL COMPUTING SERIES

Consulting Editors

DAN SIMPSON
BSc, FIMA, FBCS
Alvey Directorate

RICHARD VERYARD
MA, MSc
Data Logic Limited

The aim of this series is to address various practical issues and topics in information technology. Modern computing involves a growing number of specialist areas; it is increasingly difficult to keep one's knowledge current. The emphasis is on providing up-to-date coverage of a subject, rather than theoretical novelty. These books should be widely read by practising professionals in data processing and information technology, as well as by students on vocational courses, in order to maintain and improve professional standards of computing in industry and commerce. The authors themselves are drawn either directly from industry or are academics with first-hand industrial/commercial experience.

Other titles in the series
VERYARD: *Pragmatic Data Analysis*
TAYLOR: *PICK for Users*
WALSH: *Computer Users' Data Book*
SPENCER: *Computing Standards: A Practical Guide for Data Processing Management*
PURSER: *Computers and Telecommunications Networks*
BECKETT: *Introduction to Cryptology*

Practical Data Communications
MODEMS, NETWORKS AND PROTOCOLS

FRED JENNINGS

BLACKWELL SCIENTIFIC PUBLICATIONS

OXFORD LONDON EDINBURGH

BOSTON MELBOURNE

© 1986 by
Blackwell Scientific Publications
Editorial offices:
Osney Mead, Oxford, OX2 0EL
   (*Orders*: Tel. 0865 240201)
8 John Street, London, WC1N 2ES
23 Ainslie Place, Edinburgh, EH3 6AJ
3 Cambridge Center, Suite 208, Cambridge,
   MA 02142, USA
107 Barry Street, Carlton,
   Victoria 3053, Australia

First published 1986
Reprinted 1988, 1989

Phototypeset by
Oxford Computer Typesetting
Printed and bound in
Great Britain at
The Alden Press, Oxford

DISTRIBUTORS

USA
   Publishers' Business Services
   PO Box 447
   Brookline Village
   Massachusetts 02147
   (*Orders*: Tel: (617) 524 7678)

Canada
   Oxford University Press
   70 Wynford Drive
   Don Mills
   Ontario M3C 1J9
   (*Orders*: Tel: (416) 441–2941)

Australia
   Blackwell Scientific Publications
   (Australia) Pty Ltd
   107 Barry Street
   Carlton, Victoria 3053
   (*Orders*: Tel: (03) 347 0300)

British Library
Cataloguing in Publication Data

Jennings, Fred
   Practical data communications : modems,
   networks and protocols.
   1. Computer network protocols
   I. Title
   001.64′25   TK5105.5

ISBN 0-632-01306-0

To
Jenny and Clare

Acknowledgements

This book is an expanded, up to date version of training material known as "Jensheets". "Jensheets" were written during my employment as a Senior Consultant with Data Logic in their Professional Services Division. I wish to thank Data Logic for giving their permission to use some of the material from these "Jensheets" in this book.

I would also like to express my gratitude to J. Sagues, M.D. Richardson and R. Brace, colleagues at CASE Communications Ltd for reading the draft and providing helpful comments.

Contents

Preface

This book has the word "practical" in its title because it is written for people who are involved with data communications in their everyday lives.

It attempts to answer a basic question: "How many different ways can communicating devices be connected together for the interchange of data ?"

The hardware providing the interconnection is called a "network".

The communicating devices connected together by the "network" are assumed to be computers and terminals.

In a practical book frequent references must be made to data communications standards and Standards Organisations. In this book these organisations are referred to by their initials with their full titles listed in Appendix F.

Many references have been made to the CCITT (Consultative Committee for International Telegraph and Telephone) based in Geneva, Switzerland and part of the ITU (International Telecommunications Union). Titles of the CCITT V, X, I and G Recommendations are listed in the Appendices.

Chapter 1

Introduction

A NETWORK

A data communications network is used to connect together a number
of geographically separated computer systems and terminal systems for
the interchange of data. The size of a network can vary from a few
metres of connecting cable to a world-wide system of interconnected
equipments.

A COMPUTER SYSTEM

A computer system as described in this book can be any size from a
large main-frame computer system to a mini-computer system.

A TERMINAL SYSTEM

Terminal systems can take many physical forms but the majority provide a user with a keyboard for the input of data to the network and a
visual display unit (VDU) and/or printer for the presentation of data
output from the network. A single keyboard/VDU terminal is usually
known as a VDU or a VDT (visual display terminal).

Terminal systems of this physical form can be grouped into one of
four types:

An asynchronous terminal system comprising a single unit with an
integrated keyboard and hard-copy printer which communicates
asynchronously using start-stop character and/or block mode
transmission;

An asynchronous terminal system comprising a single VDT which
communicates asynchronously using start-stop character and/or
block mode transmission and to which a separate hard-copy printer can be connected if required;

A synchronous terminal system comprising a single VDT which
communicates using synchronous block mode transmission and to
which a separate hard-copy printer can be connected if required;

1

A synchronous terminal system (clustered display system) comprising a terminal controller unit which communicates using synchronous block mode transmission and to which are attached a number of VDTs and printers.

For brevity, computer systems and terminal systems will be referred to as computers and terminals.

NETWORK CONNECTIONS

The most common types of network connections are:

Computer to computer

Computer to one or more terminals (the most widely used)

Terminal to terminal.

For any of these connections, four essential items are required to provide a viable configuration for the transfer of data (basic configurations are discussed in Chapter 16).

A communications hardware interface is required in each computer/terminal to control one or more communications interfaces (CIs) to the network. This hardware (discussed in Chapter 2) is connected to the network by interface cables.

An end to end compatible character set (alphabet) is required to support data transfers (Chapter 2).

A dialogue (protocol) is required to co-ordinate the transfer of data across the network and provide recovery from data errors due to line noise. (Data link protocols are implemented by software that runs on a computer/terminal and are covered in Chapters 12 to 15.)

A network is required to connect together all the computers/terminals.

NETWORK TYPES

A communications network can be constructed using one or more of the following network types:

An internal network using point-to-point links to provide direct connection between one or more inhouse computers and inhouse terminals (Chapter 4);

A network based on the use of modems and leased analogue circuits; point-to-point or multipoint telephone type circuits or point-to-point wide-band circuits (Chapter 5);

A network which uses modems and switched analogue circuits (i.e. the Public Switched Telephone Network [PSTN]) and supports standby, auto-call and auto-answer operations (Chapter 5);

A network based on the use of leased digital circuits and network termination units (Chapter 6);

An Integrated Services Digital Network (ISDN) (Chapter 6);

A multiplexer based network which uses analogue/digital circuits and modems/network termination units (Chapter 7);

A Packet Switched Data Network (PSDN) based on X.25 (Chapter 8);

A Local Area Network (LAN) (Chapters 9 to 11).

MODEMS

Chapter 3 covers the different types of modems used on analogue circuits and their CCITT V-Series Recommendations.

DETAILED BREAKDOWN OF CHAPTERS

Fig. 1.1 provides a more detailed breakdown of the contents of Chapters 2 to 16.

4

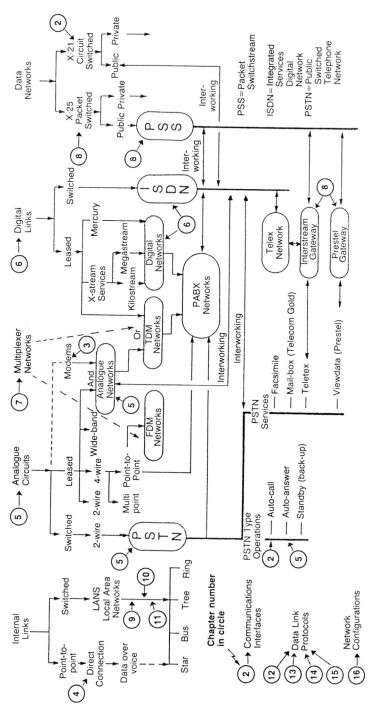

Fig. 1.1. Structure of chapters ② to ⑯.

Chapter 2

Communications Interfaces

COMMUNICATIONS CONTROLLER

Communications interfaces (referred to in this book as CIs) are used to connect a computer/terminal to a data communications network.

Standards Organisations use the abbreviations DCE (Data Circuit-Terminating Equipment) to describe the network side of a communications interface and DTE (Data Terminal Equipment) to describe the computer/terminal side of a communications interface.

The DTE side of a communications interface is operated by data communications hardware which is software controlled and forms part of a computer or terminal system.

In computer systems this hardware is modular to allow for the connection of different types and numbers of CIs. Computer manufacturers achieve this modularity in many different ways and as a consequence there is no universal name for this hardware. Typical names are:

> communications front-end processor, communications controller, communications multiplexer, communications line interface, communications adapter,

> asynchronous multiplexer, serial line asynchronous interface, asynchronous line controller, asynchronous multiple line communications coupler,

> synchronous line interface, single synchronous line interface, character synchronous interface.

In this book the term "Communications Controller" (CC) is used to describe this hardware.

The physical size of a CC depends on the number of communications interfaces that it has to the network and the complexity of the communications functions that it performs. The number of CIs can vary from just one for a terminal to several hundred for a computer. Therefore, in hardware terms a CC can take many forms.

> The CC in a terminal can be as small as a few integrated circuits (chips) sharing space with other integrated circuitry on a printed circuit board (PCB).

The CC in a mini-computer system can be one or more plug-in PCBs.

The CC in a main-frame computer system can be a separate Communications Front-End Processor (FEP) consisting of many plug-in PCBs contained in a separate cabinet.

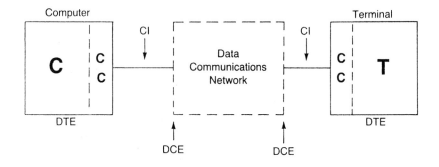

Fig. 2.1. Connection to a Network.

In Fig. 2.1, block C of the computer system and block T of the terminal system represent hardware items which, under software control, perform all the system functions excluding CC functions. Within this hardware all internal data is stored and retrieved from system memory in parallel form (typically one or more 8-bit bytes at a time).

Data communications networks normally operate using serial data transmission and the communications controller (block CC in the diagram) provides many facilities. These include parallel to serial conversion of data sent to the network (from block C or T) and serial to parallel conversion of data received from the network (to block C or T).

An in-depth understanding of a CC is not required to configure a network as long as the CC characteristics and the communications interface between the CC and the network can be defined. Fortunately the communications interface has been an area of much standardisation by American and European Standards Organisations.

MODULAR DESIGN OF COMMUNICATIONS CONTROLLER

A communications controller forming part of a computer system is normally of modular design (Fig. 2.2). The "main" hardware module controls data transfers between the computer and a number of "secondary" hardware modules. "Secondary" hardware modules connect to the "main" module and control data transfers between the communications interfaces and the "main" module.

In a minicomputer system, a "main" module is not always used, and in this case the "secondary" hardware modules connect directly to the computer.

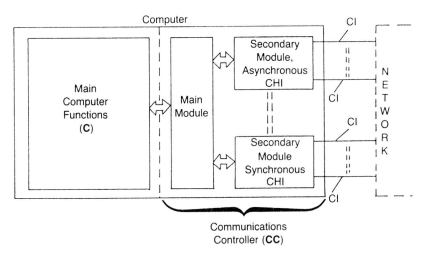

Fig. 2.2. Modular design of a CC.

"Secondary" hardware modules are normally of two types: those that operate with asynchronous CIs and those that operate with synchronous CIs.

Normally each "secondary" hardware module consists of a printed circuit board (PCB) which controls 1, 2, 4, 8, or 16 CIs. A synchronous PCB normally controls fewer CIs than an asynchronous PCB of the same size because it is designed to perform more complex functions. A PCB which controls a single CI normally has the words "line" or "interface" in its title (e.g. synchronous line interface, asynchronous interface). A PCB which controls several CIs normally has the word "multiplexer" or "multiple line" in its title (e.g. synchronous multiplexer, asynchronous multiple line communications coupler).

In this book the term "Communications Hardware Interface" (referred to as CHI) is used to describe a "secondary" hardware module which directly controls one or more communications interfaces.

ASYNCHRONOUS COMMUNICATIONS HARDWARE INTERFACE

An asynchronous CHI transmits and receives serial data via a network in start-stop format. Each serial character transmitted is preceded by a start bit (zero state) and terminated by 1, 1.5 or 2 stop bits (one state). The data transmission rate in bits per second (bit/s) is determined by the CHI. This is normally set-up on hardware straps, dual inline package (DIP) switches or by the software loading of a register. With some CHIs a single transmission rate setting determines both the transmit and receive transmission rates. Other CHIs provide separate settings for transmit rate and receive rate thus permitting split speed operation (i.e. 75/1200 bit/s or 1200/75 bit/s).

A CHI can be configured to set its bit rate automatically by the reception and inspection of a known character; this is known as automatic bit (baud) rate detection (ABR). This facility provides a computer's CHI interface with the ability to communicate with any one of a number of different terminals each operating at a different transmission rate.

The following table shows some typical asynchronous transmission rates and the number of bits per transmitted character.

Transmission Rate (bit/s)	Character Rate (ch/s)	Bits per Character	Line Code
50	6.6	7.5	ITA2
75	10	7.5	ITA2
75	7.5	10	IA5
100	10	10	IA5
110	10	11	IA5
134.5	15	9	IBM-6
150	15	10	IA5
200	20	10	IA5
300	30	10	IA5
600	60	10	IA5
1200	120	10	IA5
75/1200	7.5/120	10	IA5
1800	180	10	IA5
2400	240	10	IA5
4800	480	10	IA5
9600	960	10	IA5
19200	1920	10	IA5

For asynchronous transmission rates of 50 bit/s and 75 bit/s there is one start bit and 1.5 stop bits per serial line character and the 5-bit line code is normally the CCITT International Telegraph Alphabet No 2 (ITA2), sometimes referred to as Baudot code.

For all asynchronous transmission rates where the total number of bits per serial character is ten, the line code (7 bits plus parity bit) is normally the CCITT International Alphabet No 5 (IA5), equivalent to the American Standard Code for Information Interchange (ASCII). The parity bit can be a permanent one (mark) or a permanent zero (space) or used for odd/even character parity. Therefore parity is another parameter which must be set up in the CHI.

With asynchronous operation each serial character is individually synchronised by the use of the start-stop bits and therefore there can be a time interval between each serial character. During this time period the line signal is in the permanent "1" state.

Asynchronous terminals can operate in character mode or block mode or both.

In character mode each character is transmitted as it is typed on the keyboard and the time interval between characters is directly related to the typing speed. In this mode a CHI can be configured to provide character echo for a full-duplex character mode terminal.

In block mode the keyboard data is buffered by the terminal until a control character is typed; all the data in the buffer is then transmitted. In the transmitted serial stream the stop bit at the end of each serial ten-bit character will be followed immediately by the start bit of the next character.

SYNCHRONOUS COMMUNICATIONS HARDWARE INTERFACE

With synchronous operation each transmitted character is eight bits (no start-stop bits). A synchronous CHI sends and receives serial data via a network in blocks (frames), where each block (frame) is one continuous serial stream. Time intervals between characters in a block are not allowed.

Data sent by the CHI is normally synchronised to a transmit clock signal supplied by the network via the interface cable. Alternatively data sent by the CHI can be synchronised to an internal CHI transmit clock signal which is passed to the network.

Not all CHIs provide an internal clock and the vast majority of networks supply a transmit clock to the CHI. In this case the synchronous transmission rate is determined entirely by the transmit clock

Chapter 2

supplied by the network components (e.g. modems) and not by a combination of the CHI and the network, as is the case with asynchronous operation.

This has its advantages. Without changing the set-up of the CHI, the network link transmission rate (bit/s) can be increased by substituting a higher speed modem for a lower speed modem: also a synchronous modem can have a second, lower transmission rate for use over a temporary link (PSTN) if the main link should fail (standby operation).

The following table shows some typical synchronous transmission rates and their corresponding character rates.

Transmission Rate (bit/s)	Character Rate (ch/s)
1200	150
2400	300
4800	600
7200	900
9600	1200
12000	1500
14400	1800
16000	2000
16800	2100
19200	2400
48000	6000
56000	7000
64000	8000
72000	9000

For the same transmission rate, the corresponding serial character rate is higher for synchronous operation than for asynchronous operation. This is because of the difference in the number of bits per serial character (8 instead of 10).

The line code used for synchronous operation is usually 7-bit IA5 (ASCII) plus a parity bit or 8-bit Extended Binary Coded Decimal Interchange Code (EBCDIC). For synchronous operation odd parity is normally used with the 7-bit IA5 code.

When a CHI receives a synchronous block of data it has to search the serial stream bit by bit to find the beginning of the block. Only then can it determine the character boundaries in the serial stream and perform its serial to parallel conversion.

With control character orientated protocols the beginning of a synchronous block is marked by a number of SYN characters and for bit orientated protocols the begining of a frame is marked by a single

FLAG character. Therefore the CHI has to recognise control characters in IA5 (ASCII) or EBCDIC code in order to perform start of block recognition and other functions such as block check character (BCC) checking.

At one time CHIs were divided into two types: those used for control character orientated protocols and those used for bit orientated protocols. Now there is usually only one type of synchronous CHI which can be set up to the type of protocol and the line code to be used.

CHI line protocols and the following synchronous CHI functions are described in more detail in Chapter 12.

Control Character Orientated Operation

For control character orientated protocol operation a synchronous CHI normally performs the following functions:

The generation of SYN characters at the front of each transmitted block and the insertion of extra SYNs (SYN fill) to overcome timing difficulties (computer underrun);

The detection and stripping of the SYN characters found at the front of each received block and the stripping of SYN characters found in data as a result of a SYN fill CHI function;

Block check character (BCC) detection and generation using VRC/LRC or 16-bit CRC (this requires the detection by the CHI of control characters such as SOH, STX, ETX, ETB in either IA5 [ASCII] or EBCDIC codes; the detection of a BCC error by a CHI is normally signalled to its computer using a status bit);

In Binary Synchronous transparent mode, the detection and stripping of the first DLE of a character pair found in a received data block; during transmission the automatic insertion of an extra DLE on detecting a single DLE in a data block;

The detection and flagging to its computer of incoming data loss due to overwriting of the CHI buffer (computer overrun).

Bit Orientated Operation

For bit orientated protocol operation a synchronous CHI normally performs a number of functions:

The generation of FLAG characters at the front of each transmitted frame and between frames;

The detection and stripping of FLAG characters at the front of each received frame and between frames;

The generation and detection of an "abort" sequence of 7–15 consecutive "1" bits;

The detection and generation of the CCITT V.41 cyclic redundancy check (CRC-16);

The insertion/deletion of "0" bits to achieve data transparency.

INTERFACE CHARACTERISTICS

A CHI (DTE) connected via a CI to a network (DCE), must be compatible with the interface characteristics of the CI and the network (DCE). These interface characteristics can be considered under five main headings.

Transmission Rate

This specifies a serial transmission rate in bits per second or, for the faster interfaces, millions of bits per second (Mbit/s). For any given CI there is a theoretical maximum rate and a practical maximum rate which depends on the length of the interface cable.

Electrical

The electrical characteristics specify the polarity and the minimum/maximum values of the magnitudes of voltage/current that equate to a serial "1" condition and a serial "0" condition.

Interface Specification	Electrical characteristics		Polarity	
	Min. value	Max. value	"1"	"0"
CCITT V.28 EIA RS-232-C	3 volts	25 volts	−V	+V
EIA RS-422-A EIA RS-423-A	0.2 volt	6 volts	−V	+V
CCITT X.26 (V.10) CCITT X.27 (V.11)	0.3 volt	10 volts	−V	+V

There are two types of electrical interfaces: unbalanced interfaces and balanced interfaces.

In an unbalanced interface all the signals in the interface share a common return wire; if there are ten signals in the interface then a total of eleven wires are used.

In a balanced interface each signal in the interface has its own return wire; if there are ten signals in the interface then a total of twenty wires are used.

Balanced interfaces are superior to unbalanced interfaces because they support higher transmission rates on longer interface cables.

There are interfaces such as V.35 which use a mixture of unbalanced and balanced signals.

Functionality

This identifies the function of each interchange circuit in the interface and specifies the number of data, control and timing (clock) signals required to operate the interface.

Procedural

This describes control signals and their correct timed sequence of operation.

Mechanical

This specifies the type of interface connector, the number of pins/ sockets in the connector and the assignment of interchange circuits to pins.

The International Standards Organisation (ISO) produces standards for Computer and Information Processing. Some of these standards are concerned with DCE-DTE interface connectors and pin assignments.

ISO 2110
This standard covers the 25-pin DTE/DCE interface connector and pin assignments for CCITT V.24 interchange circuits with CCITT V.28 electrical characteristics.

ISO 2593
This standard covers the 34-pin DTE/DCE interface connector and pin assignments for CCITT V.24 interchange circuits with CCITT V.35 electrical characteristics.

ISO 4902
This standard covers the 37-pin and 9-pin DTE/DCE interface

connectors and pin assignments for CCITT V.24 interchange circuits with CCITT V.10 (X.26) or CCITT V.11 (X.27) electrical characteristics.

ISO 4903

This standard covers the 15-pin DTE/DCE interface connector and pin assignments for CCITT X.20, X.21 or X.22 interchange circuits with CCITT V.28, CCITT V.10 (X.26) or CCITT V.11 (X.27) electrical characteristics.

Appendix A and Appendix B list the CCITT V. and X. recommendations.

COMMUNICATIONS INTERFACE STANDARDS

American and European Standards bodies have agreed on a number of recommendations/specifications defining CIs.

The following list covers the most commonly used CIs.

Interface Specification European CCITT		American EIA	Synch./ Asynch.	Balanced/ Unbalanced	Max. bit/s
V.24/V.28	=	RS-232-C	A+S	U	20,000
V.25	=	RS-366-A	A	U	20,000
V.25 bis			A+S	U	20,000
		RS-449-A	A+S	U/B	2,000,000
X.26 (V.10)	=	RS-423-A	A+S	U	100,000
X.27 (V.11)	=	RS-422-A	A+S	B	10,000,000
X.21 (X.26/27)			S	U/B	48,000
X.21 bis (V.28)			S	U	9,600
X.21 bis (X.26)			S	U	9,600
X.21 bis (X.26/27)			S	U/B	48,000
X.21 bis (V.35)			S	U+B	48,000
V.35			S	U+B	168,000
Current Loop (20/60 mA)			A	B	20,000
Telegraph (80-0-80)			A	U	110
Telex (80-0-80 or SCVF)			A	U	50
(SCVF maximum)			A	U	300

RS-232-C (V.24/V.28) INTERFACE

The Electronics Industries Association (EIA) in Washington DC, USA produces interface standards. By far the most commonly used and best known of these standards is the EIA RS-232-C standard (RS stands for Recommended Standard and C refers to the revision level). The EIA RS-232-C standard defines an unbalanced interface between DTE and DCE equipment employing serial binary data interchange at transmission rates up to 20,000 bit/s. The interface operates with asynchronous and synchronous data but is limited to an interface cable length of approximately 15 metres (50 feet).

The standard is made up of seven sections which include the functional description of Interchange Circuits, Electrical Signal Characteristics and Interface Mechanical Characteristics (pin assignments).

The EIA RS-232-C standard is equivalent to:

CCITT V.24 — description of interchange circuits;

CCITT V.28 — electrical signal characteristics;

ISO 2110 — 25-pin DTE/DCE interface connector and pin assignments.

The main difference between the EIA RS-232-C standard and the CCITT V.24 recommendations is that the EIA identifies each interchange circuit by a two or three character alphabetic reference while the CCITT uses a three character numeric reference. For example, the RS-232-C reference for the transmit data interchange circuit is BA, while the CCITT V.24 reference is 103. All the V.24 references lie between 100 and 200 and are known as the 100-Series.

Figure 2.3 shows the interface connector pins and their assigned signals.

An RS-232-C interface connector (female) is normally fitted on the back of units which form components of a network. These units take many forms:

Asynchronous, asynchronous/synchronous and synchronous modems (see Chapter 3);

Equipment supplied for inhouse operation (see Chapter 4);

Network termination units used on digital links (see Chapter 6);

Asynchronous and synchronous multiplexers (see Chapter 7);

25-pin Connector Pin No.	CCITT Circuit Number	EIA RS-232-C Ref	Description of Interchange Circuit	Direction to DCE	Direction to DTE
1	–	AA	Protective Ground		
2	103	BA	Transmitted Data (TD)	X	
3	104	BB	Received Data (RD)		X
4	105	CA	Request To Send (RTS)	X	
5	106	CB	Ready For Sending [Clear To Send] (CTS)		X
6	107	CC	Data Set Ready (DSR)		X
7	102	AB	Signal Ground or Common Return		
8	109	CF	Data Channel Received Line Signal Detector (RLSD)		X
9	–	–	N (N = reserved for)		
10	–	–	N (National Use)		
11	126	–	Select Transmit Frequency	X	
12	122	SCF	Backward Channel (Secondary) RLSD		X
13	121	SCB	Backward Channel Ready (Secondary CTS)		X
14	118	SBA	Transmitted Backward Channel Data (Secondary Transmitted Data)	X	
15	114	DB	Transmitter Signal Element Timing		X
16	119	SBB	Received Backward Channel Data (Secondary Received Data)		X
17	115	DD	Receiver Signal Element Timing		X
18	141	–	Local Loopback (Loop 3)	X	
19	120	SCA	Transmit Backward Channel Line Signal (Secondary Request To Send)	X	
20	108/1	–	Connect Data Set To Line (CDSTL) *	X	
	108/2	CD	Data Terminal Ready (DTR) *	X	
21	140	–	Remote Loopback (Loop 2) *	X	
	110	CG	Data Signal Quality Detector *		X
22	125	CE	Calling (Ring) Indicator (RI)		X
23	111	CH	Data Signalling Rate Selector *	X	
	112	CI	Data Signalling Rate Selector *		X
24	113	DA	Transmitter Signal Element Timing	X	
25	142	–	Test Indicator		X

* * * Selectable

Pin Assignment Variations often used by Modem Manufacturers

9	–	–	Positive Test Voltage (USA Modems)		
10	–	–	Negative Test Voltage (USA Modems)		
9	116	–	Select Standby	X	
11	116	–	Select Standby	X	
24	116	–	Select Standby	X	
10	117	–	Standby Indicator		X
25	117	–	Standby Indicator		X
11	110	CG	Data Signal Quality Detector		X
12	110	CG	Data Signal Quality Detector		X
24	110	CG	Data Signal Quality Detector		X
25	110	CG	Data Signal Quality Detector		X

Fig. 2.3. V.24/V.28 (RS-232-C) Interface.

Network interface units used on local area networks (see Chapters 9 to 11).

V.25 (RS-366-A) AUTO-CALL INTERFACE

CCITT Recommendation V.25 covers "automatic calling and/or answering equipment on the general switched telephone network including disabling of echo suppressors on manually established calls".

V.25 specifies an auto-call unit (ACU) which enables a computer to

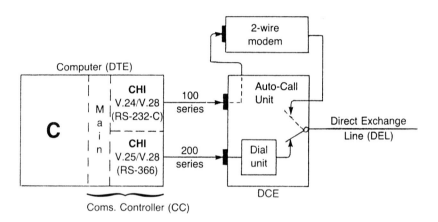

Fig. 2.4. V.25 Auto-Call Unit.

dial telephone numbers over the Public Switched Telephone Network and establish dialled connections with remote computer/terminals.

An ACU is connected to a computer by two 25-pin "D" type interface connectors as shown in Fig. 2.4. One interface uses the CCITT 100-Series interchange circuits (V.24/V.28) connected via the ACU to a modem for data transmission. The other interface uses the CCITT 200-Series interchange circuits (V.25/V.28) for automatic calling.

Interchange circuits in the 200-Series have a numeric reference between 200 and 213 (pin assignments are shown in Fig. 2.5).

The 200-Series (RS-366-A) interface is used only during call establishment and disconnection. A computer dials a telephone number by sending via the RS-366-A interface one dial digit at a time in 4-bit parallel form. After the last digit of the telephone number has been sent to the ACU, one more 4-bit code is sent to indicate end of number (EON). When a PSTN connection is established then data transmission is performed via the 100-Series interface.

Most computer manufacturers provide 200-Series (RS-366-A) interfaces and associated software for auto-calling. Until recently the standard ACU in the UK was British Telecom's Data Control Equipment (DCE) No. 1 (replaced by the Datel Autocaller). In the USA the standard ACU is the Bell 801 ACU or equivalent.

Auto-call units have been overtaken in technology by auto-dial modems which use only one RS-232-C interface for both auto-calling and data transmission (see V.25 bis).

25-pin Connector Pin No.	CCITT Interchange Circuit	EIA RS-366-A Ref	Name	Direction to	
				DCE	DTE
1	–	–	Shield (cable)		
2	211	DPR	Digit Present	X	
3	205	ACR	Abandon Call (and Retry)		X
4	202	CRQ	Call Request	X	
5	210	PND	Present Next Digit		X
6	213	PWI	Power Indication		X
7	201	SG	Signal Ground		
13	204	DSC	Distant Station Connected		X
14	206	NB1	Digit Signal Circuit	X	
15	207	NB2	Digit Signal Circuit	X	
16	208	NB3	Digit Signal Circuit	X	
17	209	NB4	Digit Signal Circuit	X	
18	–	RC	Receive Common		
19	–	SC	Send Common		
22	203	DLO	Data Line Occupied		X

Dial digits are sent to the DCE on interchange circuits 204 to 209 in four bit parallel form.

	209	208	207	206
Dial digit "0"	0	0	0	0
Dial digit "1"	0	0	0	1
Dial digit "9"	1	0	0	1
End of number digit (EON)	1	1	0	0
Separation (pause) between digits (SEP)	1	1	0	1

Fig. 2.5. 200-Series Interchange Circuits for V.25 (RS-366-A) Auto Calling.

V.25 bis AUTO-CALL INTERFACE

The V.25 bis draft recommendation covers "automatic calling and/or answering equipment on the General Switched Telephone Network (PSTN) using the 100-Series interchange circuits".

Most modem manufacturers supply modems containing integrated

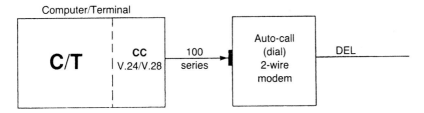

Fig. 2.6. Auto-call modem.

auto-calling circuitry. A computer/terminal (DTE) connects to a modem (DCE) via a single RS-232-C interface and can perform, through this interface, both auto call/answer and data transfer operations (see Fig. 2.6).

For auto-call operation there is a "dialogue" between the DTE and the modem and this "dialogue" varies from modem to modem.

The CCITT V.25 bis draft recommendation defines the interface between a computer/terminal (DTE) and an auto call/answer modem (DCE) and identifies two different operational modes (options).

Direct Call (Option 1)

This mode (option) uses "connect dataset to line" (CDSTL) operation and gives a calling DTE the capability of calling a pre-defined number already stored in the modem.

Addressed Call (Option 2)

This mode uses "data terminal ready" (DTR) operation and gives a calling DTE extensive call capabilities by means of instructions exchanged between the calling DTE and the modem.

As part of the automatic calling procedure, instructions (called commands) are sent by the DTE to the modem and instructions or responses (collectively called indications) are sent by the modem to the DTE. Commands and indications can be sent/received using asynchronous or synchronous operation.

With asynchronous operation each start-stop character is ten bits: a start bit, 7 bits IA5 code, even parity bit and a stop bit. With synchronous operation each character is 8 bits: 7 bits IA5 code and an odd parity bit.

The format for asynchronous operation is:

"Message" CR LF.

There are two formats for synchronous operation.
A format for control character orientated synchronous operation:

SYN SYN STX "Message" ETX.

An HDLC format for bit orientated synchronous operation:

FLAG ADDR CONTROL "Message" FCS FLAG.

A "message" is a number of 8-bit data units, where each unit consists of a 7-bit IA5 character plus an odd parity bit.

Different types of "messages" are identified by a combination of three alphabetic characters at the beginning of the "message". A "message" consists of three alphabetic characters, or three characters plus one or more parameters; each parameter is separated by a semi-colon (;).

There are over 20 different types of "messages" and the following are a few examples.

DTE to DCE Command	Modem Action
CRN "phone number"	Modem dials number
CRS "memory address"	Modem dials number stored in specified memory address
PRN "memory address" ; "phone number"	Modem stores phone number in specified memory address
RLN	Modem is requested to send list of stored phone numbers

DCE to DTE Indication	Modem Action
VAL	Modem indicates reception of a valid programming command
INV	Modem indicates reception of an invalid command
INC	Modem indicates reception of an incoming call (ringing)
LSN "memory addresses" ; "phone numbers"	Modem sends list of phone numbers in its memory

RS-449-A INTERFACE

This interface was introduced to provide greater cabling distance and faster operation than the RS-232-C interface.

The interface connector is a 37-pin connector with an additional 9-pin connector for a secondary communications channel. ISO 4902 covers 37-pin and 9-pin DTE/DCE interface connectors and pin assignments.

Figure 2.7 shows these pin numbers and their associated signals.

ISO 4902 and EIA RS-449-A pin assignments for 37-pin connector

Pin Number A	Pin Number B	ISO 4902 Cct	ISO 4902 Name	EIA RS-449-A Cct	EIA RS-449-A Name	Direction to DCE	Direction to DTE
1			Cable Shield		Shield		
2		112	Data Rate Selector (DCE)	SI	Signalling Rate Indicator		X
3			Spare		Spare		
4	22	103	Transmitted Data	SD	Send Data	X	
5	23	114	Transmit Clock (DCE)	ST	Send Timing		X
6	24	104	Received Data	RD	Receive Data		X
7	25	105	Request to Send	RS	Request to Send	X	
8	26	115	Receive Clock	RT	Receive Timing		X
9	27	106	Ready for Sending	CS	Clear to Send		X
10		141	Local Loopback	LL	Local Loopback	X	
11	29	107	Data Set Ready	DM	Data Mode		X
12	30	108/1	Connect Dataset to Line			X	
		108/2	Data Terminal Ready	TR	Terminal Ready	X	
13	31	109	Carrier Detect	RR	Receiver Ready		X
14		140	Remote Loopback	RL	Remote Loopback	X	
15		125	Calling Indicator	IC	Incoming Call		X
16		111	Rate Selector (DTE)	SR	Signalling Rate	X	
		126	Select Transmit Frequency	SF	Select Frequency	X	
17	35	113	Transmit Clock (DTE)	TT	Terminal Timing	X	
18		142	Test Indicator	TM	Test Mode		X
19		102	Signal Ground	SG	Signal Ground	X	
20		102b	DCE Common Return	RC	Receive Common		X
21			Spare		Spare		
28		135	Terminal Available	IS	Terminal in Service	X	
32		116	Select Standby	SS	Select Standby	X	
33		110	Signal Quality Detector	SQ	Signal Quality		X
34		136	New Signal	NS	New Signal	X	
36		117	Standby Indicator	SB	Standby Indicator		X
37		102a	DTE Common Return	SC	Send Common	X	

ISO 4902 and EIA RS-449-A pin assignments for 9-pin connector

Pin	ISO 4902 Cct	ISO 4902 Name	EIA RS-449-A Cct	EIA RS-449-A Name	Direction to DCE	Direction to DTE
1		Cable Shield		Shield		
2	122	Backward Carrier Detect	SRR	Sec. Receiver Ready		X
3	118	Transmitted Backward Data	SSD	Secondary Send Data	X	
4	119	Received Backward Data	SRD	Sec. Receive Data		X
5	102	Signal Ground	SG	Signal Ground		
6	102b	DCE Common Return	RC	Receive Common		X
7	120	Backward Request to Send	SRS	Sec. Request to Send	X	
8	121	Backward Channel Ready	SCS	Sec. Clear to Send		X
9	102a	DTE Common Return	SC	Send Common	X	

Fig. 2.7. EIA RS-449-A interface.

Unlike RS-232-C, which includes an electrical specification, RS-449-A has two separate specifications which cover an unbalanced electrical interface (RS-423-A equivalent to CCITT X.26 formerly V.10) and a balanced electrical interface (RS-422-A equivalent to CCITT X.27 formerly V.11). These interfaces operate with asynchronous and synchronous data at the following interface cable distances and transmission rates.

Interface	Distance in metres	Max. transmission rate
RS-423-A	10	100,000 bit/s
X.26 (V.10)	100	10,000 bit/s
	1000	1,000 bit/s
RS-422-A	10	1,000,000 bit/s
(unterminated)	100	100,000 bit/s
X.27 (V.11)	1000	10,000 bit/s
RS-422-A	10	10,000,000 bit/s
(terminated)	100	1,000,000 bit/s
X.27 (V.11)	1000	100,000 bit/s

X.21 INTERFACE

This is an "interface between data terminal equipment (DTE) and data circuit terminating equipment (DCE) for synchronous operation on public data networks".

The X.21 electrical characteristics are complex as shown in the following table.

Transmission Rate Bits per second	CHI side of Interface [DTE]	Network side of Interface [DCE]
9600 and below	X.26 (V.10) or X.27 (V.11) Unterminated or X.27 (V.11) Terminated	X.27 (V.11) Unterminated
9600 and above	X.27 (V.11) Unterminated or X.27 (V.11) Terminated	X.27 (V.11) Unterminated or X.27 (V.11) Terminated

The X.21 maximum transmission (data signalling) rate is not determined by limits imposed by the electrical characteristics of the interface but by the recommended rates for public data networks specified in CCITT recommendation X.1 (plus National variations). For synchronous operation these are

> 600 bit/s, 2,400 bit/s, 4,800 bit/s, 9,600 bit/s and 48,000 bit/s (48 kbit/s).

A DTE/DCE or DCE/DTE interconnecting cable can be unterminated or terminated by a resistance. The use of cable termination is optional and depends on the specific application. A termination should be used to preserve the signal rise time and minimise reflection at higher signalling rates (above 200 kbit/s) or at any signalling rate where the cable propagation delay is of the order of half the signal element duration. Generally a resistance in the range 100–150 ohms is used.

The mechanical characteristics and pin assignments of the X.21 connector are specified in ISO 4903 (15-pin DTE/DCE interface connector and pin assignments). The X.21 connector uses 15 pins, in X.27 each balanced circuit uses two wires (pins) designated A and B in the following table.

X.26 Pin	X.27 Pins A	B	Interchange circuit	Name	Direction to DCE	DTE
1	1			For cable shield interconnection		
2	2	9	T	Transmit	X	
3	3	10	C	Control	X	
4	4	11	R	Receive		X
5	5	12	I	Indication		X
6	6	13	S	Signal element timing		X
7	7	14	B	Byte timing		X
8	8		G	Common Return		
9, 10			Ga	DTE Common Return	X	
15	15			Reserved for future use		

The X.21 electrical specification is used in the UK as one of the interfaces to the Digital Network Services.

The procedural part of the X.21 interface specification is concerned with Circuit Switching. There are two main types of Public Data Network: those that use Packet Switching (X.25) and those that use Circuit Switching (X.21).

In the UK, British Telecom provides an X.25 public packet switching network known as Packet SwitchStream (PSS) and an Integrated Digital Access (IDA) Pilot Service which uses X.21. Further information on IDA and the PSS is in Chapters 6 and 8 respectively.

X.21 provides for the following services and facilities:

Leased circuit service

    point-to-point
    centralised multipoint

Circuit switched service

    direct call facility (equivalent to X.25 permanent virtual circuit)
    address call facility (equivalent to X.25 switched virtual circuit).

The network connection through a circuit switched network is selected using X.21 call control procedures. These call control procedures use a mixture of X.21 interface signals (interchange circuits T, R, C and I) and X.21 defined International Alphabet No. 5 (IA5) data character sequences to establish a circuit switched connection through a network. Each data character is eight bits: seven bits IA5 plus a parity bit (odd parity).

A full explanation of a call is quite complex because time-outs are involved. However a simplified sequence ignoring time-outs is shown in Fig. 2.8.

Call Control Procedure for X.21 Address Call

The following description should be used in conjunction with the simplified sequences shown in Fig. 2.8 (see Appendix I for IA5).

A calling DTE requests a network connection by signalling a "call request" (continuous zero condition on T, with C = on).

The network (DCE) indicates "proceed to select" to the calling DTE by transmitting on R a continuous 2/11 (+) IA5 character preceded by two or more 1/6 (SYN) IA5 characters with I = off.

The calling DTE transmits its call selection character sequence on T with C = on. This sequence consists of two or more 1/6 (SYN) characters followed by the X.121 address in IA5 format and terminated by one 2/11 (+) character. SYN fill is permissible between individual selection characters.

The network indicates "incoming call" to the called DTE by

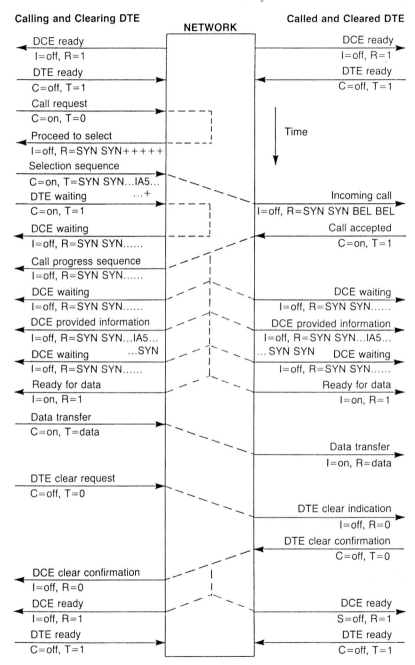

Fig. 2.8. X.21 Address Call sequence.

transmitting on R a continuous sequence of 0/7 (BEL) characters preceded by two 1/6 (SYN) characters with I = off.

The called DTE indicates "call accepted" to the network by transmitting a continuous one condition on T with C = on.

The calling DTE receives an IA5 character sequence (call progress signals) on R with I = off which either indicates that the call has been accepted or why the call has not being accepted. If accepted, the network (DCE) provides information to the calling/called DTE indicating the calling/called line identification and, as an option, information regarding charging.

The network signals "ready for data" to the calling/called DTEs (when the connection through the network has been established for data transfer) by transmitting a continuous one condition on R with I = on.

Data transfer now can take place in either or both directions.

The calling DTE initiates a network disconnection with a "clear request" (continuous zero condition on T with C = off).

X.21 bis INTERFACE

X.21 bis is a temporary alternative to X.21 and provides for the "use on public data networks of data terminal equipment (DTE) which is designed for interfacing to synchronous V-series modems".

Transmission Rates up to 9,600 bit/s

At data signalling rates of up to 9,600 bit/s the connector pin allocations and electrical characteristics of the interchange circuits are defined by the ISO 2110 standard and the CCITT V.28 recommendation or by the ISO 4902 standard and the CCITT X.26 recommendation.

Transmission Rate of 48,000 bit/s (48 kbit/s)

At data signalling rates of 48 kbit/s the connector pin allocations and electrical characteristics of the interchange circuits are defined by the ISO 2593 standard and the CCITT V.35 recommendation or by the ISO 4902 standard and the CCITT X.26/X.27 recommendation.

The connection possibilities for X.21 bis are summarised in the following table.

ISO Standard	Connector Type	Electrical Characteristics	Max. Data Rate in bit/s
2110	25 pin	V.28	9,600
4902	37 + 9 pin	V.10 = X.26	9,600
2593	34 pin	V.35	48,000
4902	37 + 9 pin	V.10/11 = X.26/27	48,000

To make an address call, an X.21 bis calling DTE must use V.25 auto-call procedures and the 200-Series interchange circuits.

There is some limited interworking through a network between an X.21 bis DTE and an X.21 DTE.

V.35 INTERFACE

V.35 specifies a synchronous interface for operation with analogue wide-band modem at a transmission rate of 48 kbit/s.

Within a network each wide-band modem link operates over a wide-band analogue circuit using a bandwidth from 60 kHz to 108 kHz; this is equivalent to the bandwidth normally used by twelve voice grade telephone circuits.

A V.35 interface uses a mixture of unbalanced (V.24/V.28) signals and balanced V.35 signals and therefore the maximum interface cable length is the same as that for V.24/V.28 (RS-232-C) (15 metres or 50 feet). The DTE/DCE interface connector is an MRAC 34-pin connector. The diameter of the pins/sockets used in the 34-way connector and the assignment of signals to the pins varies from country to country. Figure 2.9 shows the ISO 2593 connector pin assignments for the CCITT V.35 interface.

CURRENT LOOP INTERFACE

This is a very old interface type which has been used for many years to provide an inhouse point-to-point connection between a computer and a terminal over distances of several kilometres.

The interface is four wires; two wires are used to transmit data and two wires are used to receive data. The transmit current of 20 or 60 milliamps (mA) passes through the connecting network on metallic pairs without the use of any network components. A CHI to support this interface is found more often in teletype compatible visual display unit/keyboard terminals (referred to as VDUs or VDTs) than computers. For CHIs which cannot handle this type of interface there are converters available which provide RS-232-C to current loop conversion.

ISO 2593 pin assignments for 34-pin connector					
Pin Number		CCITT Interchange Circuit	Name	Direction to	
A	B			DCE	DTE
A		101	Protective Ground	X	X
B		102	Signal Ground	X	X
C		105	Request to Send	X	
D		106	Ready for Sending		X
E		107	Data Set Ready		X
F		109	Carrier Detect		X
H		108/1	Connect Data Set to Line	X	
		108/2	Data Terminal Ready	X	
J		125	Calling Indicator		X
K			F		
L			F	[F = reserved for Future	
M			F	International Standard]	
N			F		
P	S	103	Transmitted Data	X	
R	T	104	Received Data		X
U	W	113	Transmit Clock (from DTE)	X	
V	X	115	Receive Clock		X
Y	AA	114	Transmit Clock (to DTE)		X
Z			F		
BB			F		
CC			F		
DD			F		
EE			F		
FF			F		
HH			N		
JJ			N	[N = reserved for	
KK			N	National Use]	
LL			N		
MM			F		
NN			F		

Pins AA to NN are sometimes described using single lower case letters.

Each unbalanced interchange circuit with V.28 electrical characteristics uses a single pin shown under the "A" wire column.

Each balanced interchange circuit with V.35 electrical characteristics ("1" = -0.55 volt, "0" = $+0.55$ volt) uses two pins shown under the "A" wire and "B" wire columns.

To save space in the table, common names have been used for two of the interchange circuits; transmit clock and receive clock. The full names are Transmitter Signal Element Timing and Receiver Signal Element Timing respectively.

Fig. 2.9. CCITT V.35 Interface.

TELEX INTERFACE

A telex interface enables a computer/terminal to dial-up and pass telex messages to, or receive messages from, another telex subscriber.

Until mid-1983, telex operation in the UK could be considered as a form of switched telegraph operation and the telex line to a UK subscriber used 80-0-80 telegraph operation ($-80V = 1$ and $+80V = 0$) supporting serial data transmission at 50 bit/s using the International Telegraph Alphabet No. 2 (ITA2) code. Telex teleprinters with manual dial capability were provided as telex terminals and the hardware interface for 80-0-80 operation was built into the terminal system.

At one time only British Telecom could provide units to enable computers to dial telex connections via the UK telex network. The unit that British Telecom provided was the Data Control Equipment No. 3A (DCE3A) which was designed to use a telex 80-0-80 line. This unit used two interfaces to connect to the computer, a V.24/V.28 (RS-232-C) interface for data transmission and a V.25 (RS-366-A) interface for auto-call/auto-answer operation. The unit dialled telex connections by simulating the operation of a rotary manual dial and incorporated an "answerback" code.

In the UK since mid-1983, 2-wire leased telephone lines have been provided (instead of telegraph type lines) for connection to the telex network. V.21 modem frequencies are used on the line (referred to as single channel voice frequency [SCVF] operation) for serial data transmission. Dialling is performed by sending data character sequences. For operation on an SCVF 2-wire line several manufacturers now provide a telex interface unit. Some units are DCE3A compatible and others provide a single V.24/V.28 (RS-232-C) interface for computer/terminal connection.

Computers which dial connections via the telex network are mainly Message Switching Systems using message store and forward techniques.

TELEGRAPH INTERFACE

This is a very old interface type which provides full-duplex point-to-point operation over leased telegraph lines at up to 110 bit/s. Teleprinters used to be the standard terminal for telegraph line operation.

In the UK there are two charging tariffs for leased telegraph lines: Analogue H (up to 50 bit/s) and Analogue J (75 bit/s or 110 bit/s). A telegraph line does not require any additional network components (modems) at computer/terminal locations. However for CHIs which do not support a telegraph interface (line) there are converters which provide conversion between a telegraph line and a V.24/V.28 (RS-232-C) interface. In the UK, a telegraph interface uses four wires (or two wires and an earth return); two wires are used to transmit data and two wires are used to receive data. This is known as an 80-0-80 double current interface; −80 volts to line equates to a serial one and +80 volts to a serial zero. Some countries use single current interfaces, where 60 volts to line equates to a serial one and zero voltage (current) equates to a serial zero.

In the UK, single-channel voice frequency (SCVF) 2-wire telephone lines are gradually replacing 80-0-80 telegraph lines.

Chapter 3

Modems

INTRODUCTION

This chapter covers "conventional" modems used on leased lines or the Public Switched Telephone Network (PSTN). Baseband (short haul) modems are covered in Chapter 4.

A modem (modulator-demodulator) is an item of equipment which converts serial digital signals into analogue signals and vice-versa. Standards Organisations use the general abbreviations of DCE (data circuit-terminating equipment) to describe a modem and DTE (data terminal equipment) to describe a computer, terminal, or any device connected to a modem.

A modem has two interfaces, as shown in Fig. 3.1:

A DCE to analogue circuit (line) interface

A DCE to DTE multi-wire digital interface.

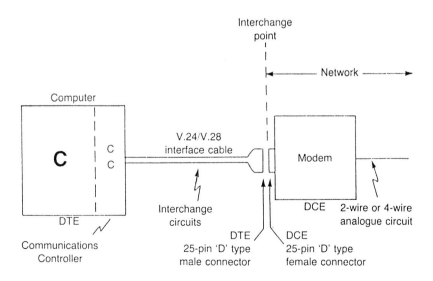

Fig. 3.1. Modem interfaces.

Standards organisations refer to each wire (conductor) in the multi-wire digital interface as an "interchange circuit". Interchange circuits are used for a mixture of data transfer, control and timing purposes.

POINT-TO-POINT LINK

The simplest network that can be constructed using modems is a point-to-point link where two modems are connected by a single communications circuit (line). In the example shown in Fig. 3.2 a "link" connects DTE (computer) to DTE (terminal) while a "line" connects DCE (modem) to DCE (modem); therefore a "link" consists of a "line" plus two modems.

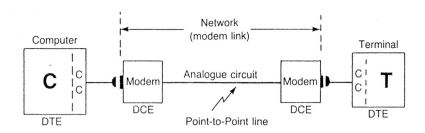

Fig. 3.2. A modem link.

TRANSMISSION RATES

At transmission rates up to 20 kbit/s the majority of modems use a CCITT V.24/V.28 (RS-232-C) interface accessed via a 25-way 'D' type female connector on the back of the modem.

At transmission rates from 48 kbit/s to 168 kbit/s wide-band modems are required which use a CCITT V.35 interface accessed via a 34-way female connector on the back of the modem.

ASYNCHRONOUS OR SYNCHRONOUS OPERATION

At transmission rates up to 20 kbit/s there are three basic types of modem.

Modems for asynchronous only operation (asynchronous modems). These modems are low speed modems and operate with asynchronous start-stop character transmission. They do not provide modem clock signals.

Modems for asynchronous or synchronous operation (asynchronous/synchronous modems). These are synchronous modems which can handle asynchronous start-stop data transmission if specific character formats are used. The total number of bits in a start-stop character must be 8, 9, 10 or 11. A modem strips off the start-stop bits before transmission and reinstates them after reception. This type of modem is basically a synchronous modem providing modem clock signals with an internal asynchronous to synchronous converter.

Modems for synchronous only operation (synchronous modems). These modems operate with synchronous block mode transmission and provide modem clock signals.

Asynchronous modems can operate at any transmission rate up to their stated maximum but asynchronous/synchronous modems and synchronous modems only operate at fixed transmission rates.

TYPE OF CIRCUIT REQUIRED

Transmission rates above 20 kbit/s require a wide-band circuit (group) and wide-band modems.

At transmission rates of 20 kbit/s and below, any one of the following five analogue telephone circuits can be used:

A 4-wire point-to-point leased (non-switched) circuit

A 4-wire multipoint leased (non-switched) circuit

A 2-wire point-to-point leased (non-switched) circuit

A 2-wire point-to-point switched circuit made by dialling a connection through the PSTN

A 4-wire point-to-point switched circuit made by dialling two separate PSTN connections; known as Dual or Double Dial-up.

FULL-DUPLEX OR HALF-DUPLEX LINK

An important consideration when selecting modems is whether the combination of modem and line provides a full-duplex link or a half-duplex link. A full-duplex link allows serial data transmission in both directions through the link at the same time while a half-duplex link allows serial data transmission in only one direction at a time. Each transmission can be a single data character, block of data or a sequence of bits/characters as used in data link protocols.

Any modem which operates on a 4-wire point-to-point circuit uses one pair (2-wires) to send and one pair to receive and is therefore capable of full-duplex operation. However modems which operate on 4-wire multipoint circuits are only capable of half-duplex operation (see Chapter 5).

Synchronous only modems operate on 4-wire point-to-point circuits and many use standby (back-up) operation over the PSTN in the event of a leased line failure. For standby operation some synchronous modems use a single dial-up connection (half-duplex operation) and others use a double dial-up connection (full-duplex operation).

There are synchronous only modems which are designed to have a short turnaround delay ("request to send" to "ready for sending" delay) for operation over multipoint circuits. They are normally called fast-poll or quick-poll modems.

Asynchronous/synchronous modems only operate on 2-wire circuits (leased or switched) and all are capable of full-duplex operation.

COMPATIBILITY WITH CCITT V-SERIES RECOMMENDATIONS

The CCITT V-Series recommendations cover data transmission over the telephone network. They include specifications for modems, interfaces, test equipment and line quality.

Compatibility between modems from different manufacturers is an important consideration and the first test for compatibility is to check the V numbers quoted by manufacturers in their modem specifications. The words "bis" and "ter" refer to the second part and the third part of the appropriate V recommendation and normally cover enhancements to the original recommendation.

The CCITT V-series recommendations are listed with comments in Appendix A and an overview is shown in Fig. 3.3.

LINE CHARACTERISTICS

Certain characteristics of an analogue line are unfavourable to modem operation. Analogue signals of different frequency (tone) travel along a line at different speeds; this is known as delay distortion. The amplitudes of different frequencies (tones) are weakened (attenuated) by differing amounts; this is known as amplitude distortion.

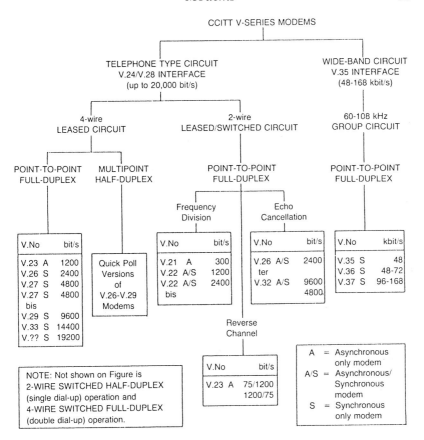

Fig. 3.3. CCITT V-Series Modems.

There are three ways of improving the characteristics of a line.

The Postal Telegraph and Telephone agency (PTT) or common carrier providing the line can condition the line.

Equalisers can be incorporated into modems to equalise the line. An equaliser is an electronic circuit with inverse characteristics to those of the analogue line. The effect of inserting one or more equalisers is to cancel out the unfavourable line characteristics and to equalise the line. An equaliser can be placed between the modulator and the line; this is known as pre-equalisation. The more common situation is to place an equaliser between the line and the demodulator; this is known as post equalisation. On a multipoint line a combination of pre and post equalisation is normally used.

A combination of line conditioning and modem equalisation can be used.

MODEM EQUALISATION

Modems use three main types of post equalisation.

Manual Equalisation

This obsolescent type of infinitely variable equalisation requires adjustments by an installation engineer to a number of equaliser controls (variables) in order to match the equaliser to the attached line. If the line is changed the process must be repeated.

Compromise Equalisation

This is similiar to manual equalisation but involves a fixed number of switch positions, each designed to match the average characteristics of a particular line type. A switch position is selected at installation time during the running of modem to modem tests. This type of equalisation is a compromise with good results on some lines and not so good on others.

Automatic Equalisation

An automatic adaptive equaliser automatically adjusts itself (trains) when receiving a special training pattern transmitted by the distant modem; no human intervention is required. After this initial adjustment the equaliser remains adaptive to any line changes by constantly training on data during normal operation. The modems retrain if they detect a marked deterioration in the line quality. Training takes place during the "request to send" to "ready for sending" time period and can be a lengthy process making this type of equalisation unsuitable for switched carrier operation on multipoint lines. Quick-poll modems are normally used on these types of line.

MODEM OPERATION

The operation of a modem can best be explained by regarding the modulator and demodulator which make up one modem as two separate items.

4-Wire Line Connection

Within the internal circuitry of a modem, a modulator uses two wires to send its modulated analogue signals to an analogue line. Similarly a demodulator uses two wires to receive modulated analogue signals from a remote modem. The connection of a modulator at one end of a line to a demodulator at the other end and vice-versa requires four wires or a 4-wire line (Fig. 3.4). On these four wires modulated carriers travel in one direction on one pair of wires and in the opposite direction on the other pair of wires.

With a 4-wire modem the internal wires from the line side of the modulator and demodulator are brought out (via internal line transformers) to a 4-wire line block or as a 4-wire line cord. The line connections are identified as "send" (modulator) and "receive" (demodulator) by marking the block or by the colour of the wires.

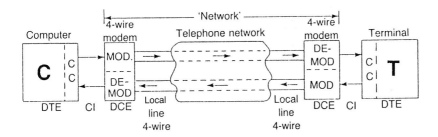

Fig. 3.4. 4-wire Connection.

2-Wire Line Connection

To connect a modem to a 2-wire line, the two internal wires from the line side of the modulator and the line side of the demodulator must be connected. They are not connected in parallel but through a 4-wire to 2-wire hybrid transformer (Fig. 3.5). In a theoretically perfect hybrid transformer, analogue signals from the modulator pass through the hybrid transformer to the 2-wire line and analogue signals from the 2-wire line pass through the hybrid transformer to the demodulator. However, in a practical hybrid transformer, low level analogue feedback occurs on the 4-wire side of the hybrid transformer from the send side (modulator) to the receive side (demodulator).

For a 2-wire only modem the hybrid transformer is part of the modem and wires from the 2-wire side of the hybrid transformer are brought out to a 2-wire block or via a 2-wire cord.

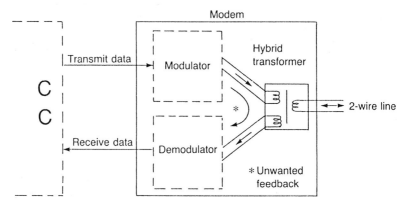

Fig. 3.5. 2-wire modem.

Small free-standing units containing hybrid transformers and switching are used to connect 4-wire only modems to 2-wire lines. They are mainly used by synchronous only 4-wire modems to provide connection to the 2-wire switched network (PSTN) for standby (back-up) purposes after the normal 4-wire leased line has failed. These units often contain V.25 auto-answer circuitry and are known by many different names. In the USA they are called "Dial Back-up Units" (DBUs).

Hybrid transformers are used in telephone exchanges to connect 2-wire leased/switched circuits from a customer's premises to "4-wire" transmission systems used by the telephone network (Fig. 3.6). In this case the internal feedback in the hybrid transformers produces echoes on telephone conversations and affects modem operation.

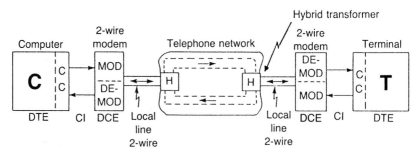

Fig. 3.6. 2-wire connection.

Operation of Interchange Circuits 103, 104 and 109

Interchange Circuit Number	Modem Pin No.	V.24/V.28 (RS-232-C) Description	Common Name	Direction to DCE	DTE
103	2	Transmitted Data	Transmit Data	X	
104	3	Received Data	Receive Data		X
109	8	Data Channel Received Line Signal Detector	Carrier Detect		X

A modulator converts a serial data stream input via the modem's transmit data interchange circuit 103 (pin 2) into a modulated analogue signal for output to the line (Fig. 3.7).

At the other end of the line the demodulator in the remote modem receives the modulated line signal and converts it into a serial data stream for output via the modem's receive data interchange circuit 104 (pin 3).

Data are carried from one modem to another modem in the form of a modulated analogue signal (carrier). One can listen with an earpiece to a modulated carrier on the line; the audible tones sound like whistles or chirps depending on the transmission rate being used and the type of modulation.

Detection of this modulated carrier by a demodulator causes the modem's carrier detect interchange circuit 109 (pin 8) to change state from off ($-V$) to on ($+V$). There is a delay, known as the carrier detect "off to on" delay, between detecting the carrier and changing the state of interchange circuit 109. There is a corresponding carrier detect "on to off" delay when the carrier is switched off at the distant end.

Within the internal circuitry of a modem, the off state of the carrier detect signal is used to clamp the receive data interchange circuit 104 (pin 3) to either a permanent "0" ($+V$) or "1" ($-V$) state. When a modem is installed the normal setting for receive data clamp is a permanent "1".

The carrier detect "off to on" delay and receive data clamp provide protection (when a carrier is absent) against short duration bursts of line noise producing spurious data on the receive data interchange circuit 104.

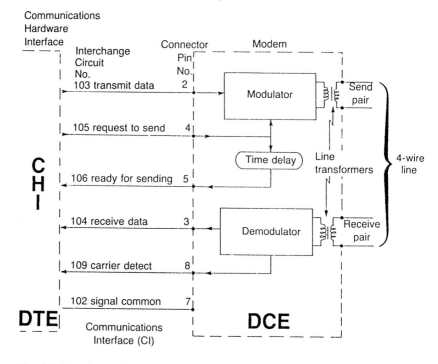

Fig. 3.7. Interchange Circuits 102-106 and 109.

Operation of Interchange Circuits 105 and 106

Interchange circuit number	Modem pin no.	V.24/V.28 (RS-232-C) description	Direction to DCE	DTE
105	4	Request to Send	X	
106	5	Ready for Sending (Clear to Send)		X

The CHI in a computer/terminal can switch on (+V) and off (−V) the "request to send" (RTS) signal on interchange circuit 105 (pin 4) to its modem. The modem uses this signal to switch on and off the analogue signals (carrier) output from the modulator to line. The RTS signal can be regarded as a modulator output enable. When the signal is on (+V) modulator analogue signals are present (enabled) and when the RTS signal is off (−V) modulator analogue signals are inhibited.

Within the internal circuitry of a modem, the RTS signal controls, via a time delay circuit, the "ready for sending" (RFS) interchange circuit 106 (pin 5). In the USA this signal is normally called "clear to send" (CTS). When RTS changes from an off (−V) to an on (+V) state the modulator output is enabled and the time delay circuit is activated. When the time delay has elapsed the RFS/CTS interchange circuit 106 changes from an off (−V) to an on (+V) state and stays on until RTS is changed back to the off state. The RTS to RFS/CTS delay is referred to as the "turnaround delay" and varies from tens of milliseconds to hundreds of milliseconds for different types of modem.

With switched carrier operation, a computer/terminal's CHI first puts RTS interchange circuit 105 (pin 4) on and then waits until RFS/CTS interchange circuit 106 (pin 5) from its modem comes on before sending data on its transmit data interchange circuit 103 (pin 2). During the RTS - RFS/CTS time period, analogue signals from the modulator are enabled and pass down the line to the demodulator in the modem at the remote end. The composition of the analogue signals during the RTS - RFS/CTS time period depends upon the type of modem.

> For an asynchronous modem (V.21 or V.23) the analogue signal is a continuous "1" frequency reflecting the "1" state of the transmit data interchange circuit 103 (pin 2) during this time. In start-stop asynchronous operation the normal serial data state between characters is a continuous "1".

> For a synchronous modem the analogue signal depends upon the type of modem/equaliser being used. It can be a continuous "1" carrier reflecting the state of the transmit data interchange circuit 103 (pin 2). However it is more likely to be a clock synchronisation pattern or an equaliser training pattern generated by the modem.

Operation of Interchange Circuits 113, 114 and 115

A modem capable of synchronous operation has three V.24/V.28 (RS-232-C) interchange circuits for modem clock operation.

Interchange Circuit Number	Modem Pin No.	V.24/V.28 (RS-232-C) Description	Common Name	Direction to DCE	DTE
114	15	Transmitter Signal Element Timing [TSET]	Transmit Clock		X
115	17	Receiver Signal Element Timing [RSET]	Receive Clock		X
113	24	External Transmitter Signal Element Timing	External Clock (Transmit)	X	

Clock signals are continuous square shaped (+V/−V) signals with a frequency equal to the synchronous transmission rate. A transmit clock is derived from a free-running accurate timing source used by the modulator of a synchronous modem; a receive clock is a modem adjustable timing source controlled by the demodulator of a synchronous modem.

A computer/terminal's CHI connected to a synchronous modem uses the transmit clock on interchange circuit 114 (pin 15) to "clock out" its serial transmit data to interchange circuit 103 (pin 2). The transmit clock determines the serial bit rate and the correct timing for each transition ("1" to "0" or "0" to "1") in the serial data stream. Each serial data transition should coincide with a −V to +V transition of the transmit clock (Fig. 3.8).

Alternatively a CHI can use its own internal clock, but must supply this clock to the modulator as an external transmit clock on interchange circuit 113 (pin 24).

A synchronous modem therefore has to be set up either to provide a transmit clock on pin 15 or to accept an external transmit clock on pin 24 (Fig. 3.9).

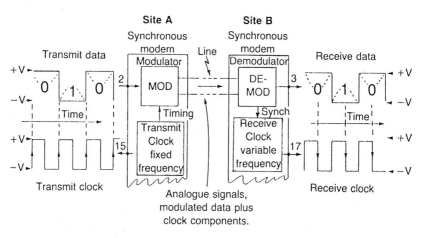

Fig. 3.8. Modem clock operation.

The receive clock interchange circuit 115 (pin 17) is used by a CHI to sample (clock) the serial data on the receive data interchange circuit 104 (pin 3). If the receive clock is synchronised then each +V to −V transition of the clock signal will coincide with the centre of a serial data bit and allow the received data to be read by the CHI as ones and zeros

(Fig. 3.8). A CHI normally requires other modem control signals, including carrier detect, to be "on" in order for it to read data from a modem.

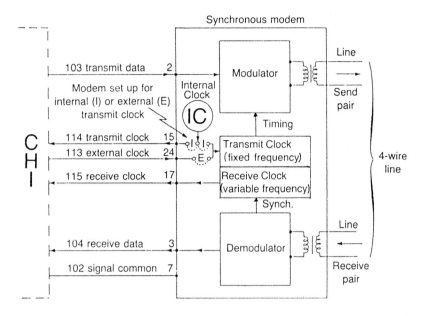

Fig. 3.9. Internal/external transmit clock.

During modem operation the demodulator in a modem continually adjusts its receive clock to keep it in synchronisation with the transmit clock in the modem at the other end of the link. The demodulator performs this task by extracting clock frequency components from modulated analogue line signals received from the distant modulator. If a point-to-point 4-wire line connecting two synchronous modems fails, then the receive clocks in each of the modems lose synchronisation with the transmit clocks at the distant ends and drift off frequency. When the line is restored the receive clocks re-synchronise.

On a point-to-point link using switched carrier operation, only the demodulator in the modem receiving the carrier has its receive clock synchronised.

With switched carrier operation, synchronous modems always synchronise their clocks during the "request to send" to "ready for sending" time period immediately before each data block transmission.

Once the modems at each end of a link are clock synchronised then the CHIs connected to the modems have to establish character synchronisation by inspecting the receive data serial stream for special data characters (SYN or FLAG) on the front of a data block transmission (see Chapter 12).

Operation of Interchange Circuits 107, 108 and 125

Interchange circuit number	Modem pin no.	V.24/V.28 (RS-232-C) description	Direction to	
			DCE	DTE
107	6	Data Set Ready		X
108/1	20	Connect Data Set To Line	X	
108/2	20	Data Terminal Ready	X	
125	22	Calling Indicator		X

These three modem interchange circuits are mainly used for auto-answer operation on the PSTN and their operation is described in Chapter 5.

FULL-DUPLEX 4-WIRE OPERATION

All 4-wire modems provide full-duplex operation on 4-wire point-to-point lines because they can use the whole bandwidth of each pair of wires. It therefore seems pointless to use switched carrier operation and switch on and off "request to send" for each transmission. Modems for use on 4-wire point-to-point circuits are normally set up for constant (continuous) carrier operation in both directions and can provide zero time delay between RTS and RFS/CTS should the computer or terminal require to use these signals.

HALF-DUPLEX 4-WIRE OPERATION

British Telecom provides leased 4-wire multipoint circuits which use branching equipment and therefore support only half-duplex modem operation. For example, consider a single multipoint circuit which is being used to allow a computer to communicate with a number of terminal clusters in different geographical locations. Constant carrier can be used in the direction from the computer to the terminal clusters but switched carrier must be used by each terminal cluster when it wishes to send. The computer instructs each terminal cluster in turn when to send its data by sending a poll "message" which includes a terminal cluster identity. (Multipoint circuits are discussed in Chapter 5.)

FULL-DUPLEX 2-WIRE OPERATION

There are three techniques for obtaining full-duplex operation over a 2-wire circuit and these are echo cancellation, frequency division and reverse channel operation.

Echo Cancellation

This is a new technique only made possible by the use of micro-processors in modem design. Echo cancellation makes it possible to use all of the line bandwidth for simultaneous transmission in both directions. This is accomplished by cancelling the echo on a 2-wire circuit that would otherwise corrupt the line signal.

Echo is mainly caused by telephone line reflections. One source of these is the hybrid transformer used in modems and telephone exchanges to convert 4-wire connections into 2-wire connections and vice-versa. An echo cancellation modem has to isolate the signal received from the remote modem by "subtracting" the interference caused by its own transmit signal as well as low-level echo signals. These echo signals emanate from the local telephone exchange and to a lesser extent from the remote end telephone exchange involved in the 2-wire connection. Cancellation of echoes is possible because of the difference in time between the original signal and the echo due to line propagation delays. An echo cancelling modem generates a copy of the echo of the original signal and subtracts it from the received line signal to produce only the original signal.

Echo cancellation will be used in the new family of V.32 modems which will offer 9600 bit/s and 4800 bit/s asynchronous/synchronous full-duplex operation over a 2-wire circuit.

Frequency Division

Frequency division is used by the V.21, V.22 and V.22 bis modems. These modems divide the bandwidth of a 2-wire line into two channels; one for transmitting and one for receiving.

A CCITT V.21 modem uses frequency shift keying (FSK) modulation to provide 2-wire full-duplex asynchronous operation at up to 300 bit/s.

CCITT V.22 and V.22 bis modems use differential phase shift keying (DPSK) modulation to provide full-duplex 2-wire asynchronous/synchronous operation at 1200 bit/s and 2400 bit/s respectively.

V.21 Modem Operation

In a full-duplex 2-wire modem using frequency division the bandwidth of the line is shared between transmission in one direction and transmission in the other direction. In telephony, tones of different pitch (frequency) can pass along a 2-wire connection in different directions without affecting each other.

This principle can best be explained by considering two telephones; one at point A and one at point B connected through the PSTN. If a person at point A whistles a high note through his/her telephone and a person at point B whistles a low note then these two notes can simultaneously pass along the connecting 2-wire line without interfering with each other. In communications terms this is full-duplex operation.

All V.21 300 bit/s modems use this principle except that instead of using single notes, they use a pair of adjacent high notes and a pair of adjacent low notes. The lower note of each pair is used to transmit/ receive a binary one and the upper note is used to transmit/receive a binary zero. This type of modulation is known as frequency shift keying (FSK) and the actual frequencies used are as follows:

Modem A to Modem B		Modem B to Modem A	
ONE	ZERO	ONE	ZERO
980 Hz	1180 Hz	1650 Hz	1850 Hz

The frequency bandwidth of the 2-wire line is split by each modem into two separate transmission paths; one path is used to transmit data and one path is used to receive data.

In the particular case of the V.21 300 bit/s modems there are effectively two modulators and two demodulators inside each modem. By using one modulator (M1) and one demodulator (D1) a modem can transmit using the low frequency pair and receive using the high frequency pair. Conversely by using modulator (M2) and demodulator (D2) a modem can transmit using the high frequency pair and receive using the low frequency pair. For two modems to communicate over a 2-wire line, one modem will use M1/D1 and the other modem will use M2/D2.

There is a convention as to which modulator/demodulator should be used at any given time and this is defined by the terms "originate" mode and "answer" mode.

If point A dials up point B over a switched line then point A is the "originator" and the modem at point A uses the "originate" mode of operation (M1/D1). If point B answers the call, then the modem at point B uses the "answer" mode of operation (M2/D2).

When a modem is powered-up it is in "originate" mode. A modem connected to a switched line (PSTN) switches into "answer" mode when it detects ringing. When a switched line connection between two modems is disconnected the modem which is in "answer" mode reverts to "originate" mode.

In computer centres which are frequently accessed by remote V.21 modem users, the modems are normally "set up" to be permanently in the "answer" mode. A remote user uses a V.21 modem in "originate" mode or an acoustic coupler connected to the telephone.

Acoustic couplers which are V.21 compatible are usually supplied in three models:

"Originate" only model, i.e. M1/D1

"Answer" only model, i.e. M2/D2

"Originate/answer" model, i.e. switchable M1/D1 or M2/D2.

It should now be obvious that two users each with an "originate" only acoustic coupler cannot communicate with each other; one must be in "answer" mode.

A CCITT V.21 modem or compatible acoustic coupler cannot communicate with an American Bell 103 standard 300 bit/s dataset (modem) because these modems use incompatible modem frequencies.

Acoustic couplers are not as popular as they once were. This is due to the low price of asynchronous modems (LSI technology) and the ease with which they can be connected to the UK PSTN due to the introduction of the new telephone plug. Many new style telephone handsets are not compatible with the acoustic chambers of a coupler.

Reverse Channel Operation

At the extreme bottom or top of the frequency bandwidth of a 2-wire telephone line there is normally sufficient bandwidth available to support a low data rate channel (as well as the normal data channel). This low rate channel is known by various names: reverse, supervisory, return, side, back, backward.

In the V-series modems this channel occupies some bandwidth below the normal data channel and operates at 75 bit/s using frequency shift keying.

In the UK when operating over a switched 2-wire line (PSTN) the reverse channel is immediately below one of the two inband signalling channels used by the PSTN for connecting and clearing PSTN connections.

2-WIRE LEASED/SWITCHED BANDWIDTH ALLOCATION

Reverse Data Channel	[PSTN only] Inband Signalling	Forward Data Channel	[PSTN only] Inband Signalling
75 bit/s		Asynchronous 1200 bit/s	
"1" "0"			
		Synchronous 2400 bit/s	
390 Hz 450 Hz		plus higher rates	

In the asynchronous V.23 modem a reverse channel can be used with a forward data channel of 1200 bit/s to provide split speed full-duplex 2-wire operation at 75/1200 bit/s and 1200/75 bit/s. This type of modem operation is used over the PSTN with British Telecom's Prestel (Viewdata) service where the user's keyboard data is input to Prestel at 75 bit/s and Prestel outputs its data at 1200 bit/s to the user's screen.

Reverse channel operation is also used extensively by synchronous modems operating on 4-wire point-to-point or multipoint circuits as the means of conveying information between a network management printed circuit board fitted in a modem and a central modem network management system.

On a 4-wire point-to-point circuit a modem using reverse channels can provide full-duplex operation on its main data channel plus full-duplex 75 bit/s operation on its two reverse channels.

HALF-DUPLEX 2-WIRE OPERATION

One method of providing 2-wire operation is to have a modem carrier on in only one direction at a time. This only supports half-duplex operation.

To implement half-duplex switched carrier operation, a data link protocol is required to control the interaction between the two ends.

Protocols are described in Chapters 12 to 15.

Assuming a computer/terminal has permission to send, then it uses its communication hardware interface (CHI) and connected modem to perform the following steps:

Change the "request to send" (RTS) signal on interchange circuit 105 (pin 4) from off (−V) to on (+V) to switch on the modem's carrier;

Wait for the "ready for sending" (RFS/CTS) signal on interchange circuit 106 (pin 5) to change from off to on;

Send a data block/frame to "transmit data" interchange circuit 103 (pin 2) (In the case of a synchronous modem the "transmit clock" interchange circuit 114 [pin 15] is normally used to clock out the "transmit data");

Switch off the modem carrier by changing RTS from on (+V) to off (−V). The modem responds by immediately changing RFS/CTS from on (+V) to off (−V).

The computer/terminal at the remote end uses its CHI to perform the following steps with its modem:

Wait for "carrier detect" (CD) on interchange circuit 109 (pin 8) to change state from off (−V) to on (+V);

Read the data from "receive data" interchange circuit 104 (pin 3) (in the case of a synchronous modem, the "receive clock" interchange circuit 115 [pin 17] is used to clock the "receive data");

Wait for "carrier detect" (CD) on interchange circuit 109 (pin 8) to change state from on (+V) to off (−V).

The remote computer/terminal can now switch on its modem's carrier and send data in the opposite direction and the procedure repeats.

MULTI-PORT MODEMS

A multi-port modem is a synchronous only modem which operates at bit rates from 4800 bit/s to 19,200 bit/s. It consists of a synchronous modem and a bit interleaved time division multiplexer in one enclosure. Each port requires one 25-pin V.24/V.28 (RS-232-C) connector on the back of the modem. For example, a 9600 bit/s modem can have four ports each operating at 2400 bit/s. Typical multi-port configurations are shown on the next page.

Modem Speed bit/s	Number of ports and speed per port	Modem Speed bit/s	Number of ports and speed per port
4800	2 @ 2400	14,400	1 @ 4800 + 1 @ 9600
7200	1 @ 2400 + 1 @ 4800	14,400	2 @ 7200
7200	3 @ 2400	14,400	3 @ 4800
9600	2 @ 4800	14,400	4 @ 2400 + 1 @ 4800
9600	1 @ 2400 + 1 @ 7200	14,400	6 @ 2400
9600	2 @ 2400 + 1 @ 4800		
9600	4 @ 2400		

ERROR-CORRECTING MODEMS

The following techniques are used in modems to overcome data errors due to line noise.

Asynchronous modems are available which operate over point-to-point links and provide a single error-free asynchronous channel. They use an ARQ type protocol and hold (buffer) their transmitted data at the sending end until an acknowledgement or request for retransmission is made by the receiving end.

Synchronous modems are available which operate at 9600 bit/s to 19,200 bit/s and use "trellis coded modulation" to provide forward error correction of synchronous data. This modulation employs an error protection scheme of interweaving (or trellising) additional bits into the transmitted data stream. These added bits allow the receive end to choose those bits which most accurately represent the original transmitted data.

DATA COMPRESSION DEVICES

Data compression units are available as free-standing units or integrated into synchronous modems. They use adaptive algorithms to compress data before transmission; the data is expanded after reception. They can operate with character or bit orientated synchronous protocols or asynchronous data. Compression can be by one half to one third. For example 19,200 bit/s can be sent/received through a 9,600 bit/s modem.

ASYNCHRONOUS TO SYNCHRONOUS CONVERSION

Asynchronous to synchronous converters are available for connecting an asynchronous computer to an asynchronous terminal via a synchronous modem link.

At each end of the modem link an external converter is connected between the asynchronous V.24/V.28 (RS-232-C) interface of a computer/terminal and the synchronous V.24/V.28 interface of a modem. The majority of converters do not require A.C. mains power but operate from D.C. power obtained from the V.24/V.28 interface signals.

Converters can provide half or full-duplex asynchronous operation at bit rates from 300 to 19,200 bit/s with start–stop character formats of 10/11 bits. As asynchronous data passes through a converter it is buffered in an internal buffer to overcome small timing differences between the asynchronous and synchronous bit rates. Larger timing differences are overcome by adding and deleting stop bits to/from the asynchronous data as it passes between converters.

The V.22, V.22 bis and V.32 asynchronous/synchronous modems contain integrated converters for asynchronous operation at 1200 bit/s, 2400 bit/s and 4800/9600 bit/s respectively.

MODEM/PORT SHARING UNIT

This is a free-standing mains powered unit which allows several asynchronous or synchronous DTEs (terminals) to share one modem or computer port. It is known by many names:

Modem expander
Port sharing unit
Digital sharing device
Modem contention unit
Multiple access unit.

This unit is used on networks which use poll/select protocols. It can connect many single terminals or cluster controllers to either one synchronous computer port at a computer centre or to one synchronous modem at a remotely connected site.

A unit is fitted with many V.24/V.28 (RS-232-C) 25-way connectors, one is used for the modem or computer port connection and the remainder (usually four) are used for the connection of DTEs (terminals). Units can be cascaded to provide more terminal connections.

A poll received by the unit is passed to all connected terminals. A responding terminal or cluster controller switches on "request to send" to seize the send path through the unit. This send path is maintained during data transmission until the terminal switches off "request to send". A unit incorporates round robin priority logic which prevents any connected terminal in a polled group from hogging the send path.

Chapter 4

Direct Connection

INTRODUCTION

This chapter describes how computers and terminals can be directly connected to one another by inhouse point-to-point communications links when physically separated by distances varying from several metres to many kilometres. With this type of connection the computers and terminals are all located in the same room, building or campus.

These types of network used to be called "inhouse networks" and have been in existence for over twenty years and therefore predate Local Area Networks (LANs).

LANs (Chapters 9 to 11) offer a greater degree of interconnection and operate at transmission rates from 100 kbit/s to 10 Mbit/s over the interconnecting medium.

Reference will be made to the various types of computer/terminal hardware communications interfaces (CHIs) and specialised products that can be used.

DIRECT CONNECTION USING MULTI-WIRE CABLES

Asynchronous Operation Using Direct Connect Cables

The simplest inhouse "network" is a single direct connect RS-232-C cable connecting together a computer and a terminal by their asynchronous V.24/V.28 (RS-232-C) interfaces. Direct connect interface cables are normally provided in various fixed lengths up to a maximum length. The V.28 (RS-232-C) specification does not specify a maximum length of cable but does specify a maximum value of cable capacitance (2500 pF). Interface cables vary in their capacitance per metre length but the normally accepted maximum cable length which meets the specification is around 15 m (50 ft). The V.28 specification applies to serial transmission rates up to and including 20,000 bits per second. The higher the bit rate the more the serial interface signal is degraded by cable capacitance. Special low capacitance RS-232-C direct connect interface cables are available which operate quite satisfactorily at 9600 bit/s over distances up to 150 m.

Asynchronous Operation Using Modem Cables

Modem interface cables which connect asynchronous computer/terminal V.24/V.28 (RS-232-C) interfaces to modems cannot be connected together to form a direct connection for two reasons.

The 25-way D type connectors on the ends of the modem interface cables are the same sex. V.24 connectors (25-pin D type) used on modems are "female" (they use sockets) and V.24 connectors used on the ends of modem cables are "male" (they use pins).

The V.24 interface signals do not match up. For example, on an asynchronous modem link the computer sends data to its modem on D connector pin 2 (transmit data) and this is received by the terminal from its modem on pin 3 (receive data).

An asynchronous direct connection can be constructed from a computer modem cable and a terminal modem cable by connecting the cables together using a cross-over cable, as shown in Fig. 4.1.

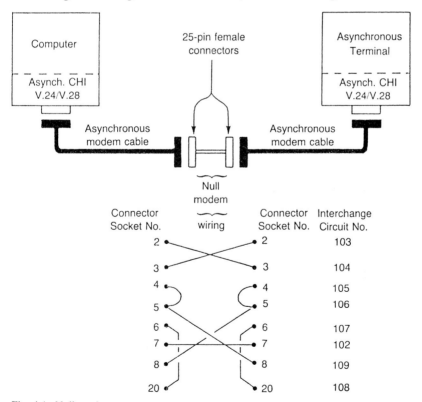

Fig. 4.1. Null modem.

This small cable consisting of two cross-connected "female" D type connectors is sometimes called a "null modem". To prevent the cables coming apart after connection a "null modem" should provide screw or clip retention compatible with the connectors on the modem cables.

Synchronous Operation Using Modem Cables

A V.24/V.28 (RS-232-C) synchronous interface within a computer/terminal requires two interface signals for correct operation; transmit clock (pin 15) and receive clock (pin 17). These clock signals are normally provided by a synchronous modem connected to a computer/terminal via a synchronous modem interface cable. A synchronous modem cable normally contains more wires than an asynchronous modem cable because clock signals are not required for asynchronous operation. A null modem is unsuitable for direct connection using synchronous modem cables because it cannot supply the clock signals.

A specialised unit is needed to provide clock signals for this type of direct connection. There is no standard term for this type of unit but commonly used names are synchronous modem simulator and modem eliminator. A modem eliminator has two female 25-pin connectors and functions like two synchronous modems back to back on a very short 4-wire line. A unit provides modem type clock signals and a cross-over connection so that standard synchronous modem interface cables can be used (Fig. 4.2). If a modem eliminator regenerates the interface signals while performing a cross-over connection then each synchronous modem cable can be up to 15 m long (total length 30 m). If it does not regenerate the interface signals then the total length of both cables cannot exceed 15 m. The synchronous clocks provided by a modem eliminator can be set to operate at 2400, 4800, 9600 or 19,200 bit/s. A modem eliminator is normally supplied as a mains powered unit in a modem type enclosure. However the latest designs are only 15 cm (6 in.) long, with connectors at each end, take their power via the interface cables and need no mains power.

Many computers provide a synchronous clock on Pin 24 of their V.24/V.28 (RS-232-C) interface and this is used in conjunction with a single synchronous direct connect cable (incorporating cross-over) to connect together a synchronous computer port and a synchronous terminal.

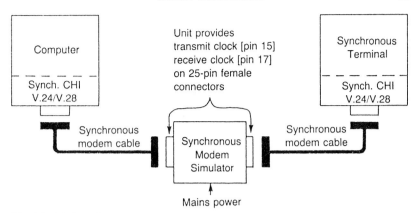

Fig. 4.2. Modem Simulator.

DIRECT CONNECTION USING LONG-LINE INTERFACES

As described in Chapter 2, the EIA RS-449-A interface with its unbalanced RS-423-A and balanced RS-422-A electrical characteristics can drive longer multi-wire interface cables than the V.24/V.28 (RS-232-C) interface. Computer and terminal equipments are appearing with these new interfaces and should be considered (on cost grounds) for asynchronous links of up to 1000 m because additional equipment is not required. CCITT X.26 (previously V.10) is equivalent to RS-423-A and CCITT X.27 (previously V.11) is equivalent to RS-422-A.

Serial line converters are available which convert a standard RS-232-C interface into an RS-422-A interface. A long-line asynchronous link can be constructed by using a converter at each end of the link.

DIRECT CONNECTION USING SPECIAL INTERFACES

There are two types of long-line asynchronous interfaces which are not RS-449-A compatible. They provide direct connection using simple 3/4-wire connections.

Some computer manufacturers provide a special communications hardware interface for their own computers/terminals which operates at transmission rates up to 9600 bit/s. This serial interface uses a single (daisy-chain) cable to connect a number of terminals in different locations to one computer port. This arrangement is really a form of inhouse multi-drop network (without modems) and requires the use of an asynchronous poll/select protocol to enable the computer to send/receive data to individual terminals. There is usually a limit of around 300–400 m for the total length of the daisy chained interface cable. An example of this type of interface is the Burroughs TDI (2-wire direct interface); a TDI/ RS-232-C interface converter is available.

The 20/60 mA current loop interface was one of the first interfaces used to provide an inhouse asynchronous link between computers and terminals over distances of up to several kilometres. The interface uses four wires, two to transmit and two to receive. The interface was very popular with VDU manufacturers; converters (RS-232-C to/from current loop) are available for computers/terminals which do not support the current loop interface.

DIRECT CONNECTION USING SPECIALISED PRODUCTS

A wide range of specialised communications products is available for the direct connection of computers/terminals with V.24/V.28 (RS-232-C) interfaces. These products provide an inhouse direct connection where the distances between computers/terminals are too great for multi-wire cables (15 metres).

These products normally operate in pairs, one at either end of a communications medium . The connecting medium can be:

An inhouse 4-wire line (cable) installed by the supplier or the customer (or existing PBX extension wiring or internal wiring);

Fibre-optic cables where there is an electrically noisy environment;

Internal mains power wiring (known in the USA as Carrier-Current Systems);

Laser beams where the link has to be made between buildings separated by a large expanse of open ground;

Micro-wave (radio) link.

Products for Use on 4-Wire Lines

There are many products specifically designed for use with short distance (short haul) 4-wire lines which cannot be connected to long distance (long haul) telephone lines. These products are cheap "modem replacements" and provide a V.24/V.28 (RS-232-C) interface. They are connected by a 4-wire line which is installed either by the product supplier, the PTT or the customer. An important point regarding the 4-wire line is that it must be a "wires only" line. In the UK this "wires only" aspect is covered by the British Telecom EPS.8 specification and in the USA by the Bell Reference PUB 43401 "Transmission Specifications for Private Line Metallic Circuits". A British Telecom supplied 4-wire line can be connected via a local telephone exchange providing it meets the EPS.8 specification. Products which connect to PTT provided lines normally require PTT approval.

Some products use modulation techniques (like modems) and can operate over longer 4-wire lines than other products. However the design aim is the same; to provide a point-to-point extended connection between a computer port and a terminal port. These products are known by various names:

Baseband modem
Limited distance modem
Short haul modem
Local modem
Line driver
Long line driver.

If these products did not exist then modems (which are more expensive) would have to be used. In the UK there does not appear to be a collective name for these products; in the USA they are known as Short Haul (SH) devices. In this chapter they will be known as SH units.

At one time all SH units were contained in small free-standing metal or plastic boxes but some of the units have now been made even smaller by incorporating them into the bodies of 25-pin connectors. When a significant number of the larger units are sited together, such as the location of a computer system, they are usually supplied as rack mounted items to save space.

SH units are available in asynchronous only, synchronous only or asynchronous/synchronous models. They operate at transmission rates from 600 bit/s to 19,200 bit/s and are used for the following reasons.

They can extend an inhouse RS-232-C asynchronous/synchronous interface between a computer port and a terminal port from the normal direct connect cabling limit of 15 metres to a maximum distance of several kilometres. Two SH units of the appropriate model are required, one at each end of a 4-wire line (wires only).

They can provide an asynchronous/synchronous inhouse multi-drop configuration. For each multi-drop link one SH unit is required at the computer end and one SH unit is required at each terminal location. A 4-wire line (wires only) is connected between each SH unit in the form of a daisy-chain. A poll/select type protocol is required to allow the computer to address each terminal.

A pair of synchronous SH units can replace a pair of normal synchronous modems on an inhouse multiplexer link. For more information on multiplexers see Chapter 7.

In a distributed communications network, where terminals are located in remote geographical locations, SH units can be used to extend the V.24/V.28 (RS-232-C) interface between a remote modem and its terminal (Fig. 4.3). One SH unit is connected to the modem by a special cross-over cable and the other SH unit is connected to the terminal using its modem interface cable.

If the remote modem is a synchronous modem then there are slight complications due to modem clocking. Both the synchronous modem and the SH unit connected to it have to be configured to use "external transmit clock" operation.

This method of extending a modem interface is sometimes called "onward linking". In the USA, products designed to connect a synchronous modem to a SH unit are called "tail circuit adaptors".

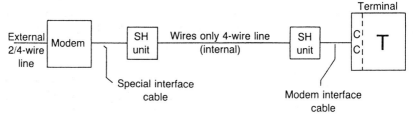

Fig. 4.3. Onward linking at remote site.

Products for Use on PBX Lines

Data over voice equipment (DOVE) saves the cost, time and effort involved in installing internal lines for data transmission links between computers and terminals. It enables existing wiring (extension lines) between PBX telephones and the PBX Master Distribution Frame

(MDF) to be used for the dual purpose of data transmission and normal telephone operation. The topology of telephone extension wiring is a star, the centre of the star is the PBX (PABX) with lines radiating out to telephone locations. Figure 4.4 shows a typical extension line connecting a telephone to a PBX.

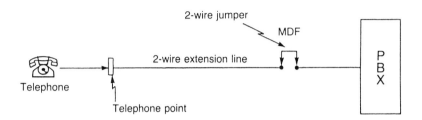

Fig. 4.4. Typical PBX extension line.

DOVE Operation

The bandwidth of a PBX extension line is about 200,000 Hz, and part of the bandwidth above the voice channel is used by DOVE to implement a full-duplex data channel. Two separate modem type channels are added above (over) the voice channel and are used for data transmission; one channel in each direction. The two channels use frequency shift keying (FSK) modulation and originate/answer modes of operation (same principle as V.21 modem operation see Chapter 3). The FSK carrier frequencies for the two data channels are not standardised and vary between products.

Medium speed DOVEs provide asynchronous or synchronous operation at transmission rates up to 19,200 bit/s and higher speed DOVEs provide synchronous operation up to 64 kbit/s.

DOVE comprises two different items of equipment.

One item is a small free-standing "subscriber unit" which has a standard telephone cord and plugs into an existing telephone extension point. The subscriber unit provides a telephone compatible connector for the connection of a normal extension telephone and a V.24/V.28 (RS-232-C) 25-pin connector for the connection of a terminal. A subscriber unit is known by other names, e.g. access unit, voice/data multiplexer.

The other item is "central equipment" usually located in the room which contains the PBX's Master Distribution Frame (MDF), or with the computer system (multiplexer, terminal controller etc.) to which the terminals are to be connected. Connection to PBX extensions is made at the MDF by removing two-wire jumpers linking the PBX to extensions and connecting in the central equipment (see Fig. 4.5). This allows modulated data signals from the central equipment and speech from the PBX to pass simultaneously along the extension lines to the subscriber units. Each subscriber unit separates the speech and the modulated data signals using low-pass and high-pass filters.

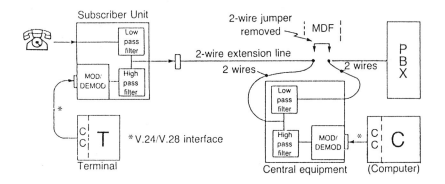

Fig. 4.5. Dove configuration.

The central equipment is connected to the MDF by a multi-core twisted pair cable; each extension line uses two pairs. This cable runs from the MDF to the central equipment, normally located next to the computer system. Some manufacturers split their central equipment into two parts. One part (passive filters) is installed in the MDF and this is connected by cable to the other part (modulator/demodulators) located with the computer system (Fig. 4.6). This splitting of the equipment halves the number of pairs required in the cable (one pair per extension line) and reduces the length of the voice path between the PBX and subscriber units.

If the distance between MDF and central equipment is too great for a cable run, then the central equipment can be located with the MDF and directly connected to the computer system by a multiplexer link.

The central equipment is modular and for each subscriber unit containing a data modulator/demodulator there is a corresponding data modulator/demodulator in the central equipment. Some manufacturers provide subscriber unit to subscriber unit operation and in this case

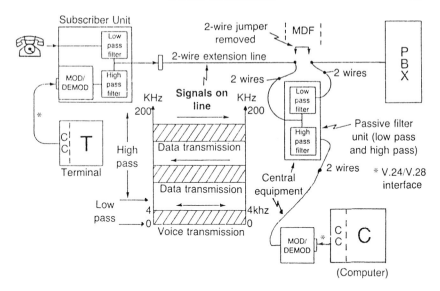

Fig. 4.6. Dove Configuration with distributed central equipment.

there are no modulator/demodulators in the central equipment. For this type of operation one subscriber unit uses originate mode and the other answer mode.

Manufacturers quote a maximum distance for DOVE operation over PBX extension lines. This maximum distance depends on the line attenuation which in turn is related to the diameter of the extension wire. Typical figures are:

Wire diameter	Max distance
0.9 mm	3.4 km
0.6 mm	2.0 km
0.4 mm	1.0 km

DOVE Configurations

DOVE can provide inhouse point-to-point links between a computer system and terminals located at telephone extension points. The transmission medium used in the links is a combination of PBX extension lines and twisted pairs in a multi-core cable. For long runs between the MDF and the computer system a multiplexer link can be used instead of the multi-core cable. The choice is one of convenience and cost.

DOVE can provide the radial connections to a star shaped Local Area Network (LAN). "Switching equipment" connected to DOVE central equipment can provide devices connected to subscriber units with access to a wide range of inhouse and/or remote services. This is a very generalised description covering a wide range of applications. Typical "switching equipment" is a statistical multiplexer providing access via user switching to services supported by computer systems at remote/inhouse locations.

Another example is a "terminal concentrator" providing connection to a LAN and enabling terminal users to access servers (see Chapter 7 and Chapters 9 to 11 covering Multiplexer Networks and LANs).

DOVE can provide a point-to-point or multipoint link between devices (computer/ terminals) connected to subscriber units. For communication between subscriber units, one unit must be in originate mode and the other unit in answer mode. For multipoint operation one device is the master and the remainder are slaves. A poll/select protocol is used to control the transfer of data between the master and slaves. Switched carrier is used by the slaves.

V.35 Compatible Products for Use on Inhouse Cables

A V.35 interface is normally used for operation with wide-band modems. However there are synchronous SH products available for connection to computer/terminal V.35 interfaces which provide synchronous full-duplex point-to-point inhouse operation at 48–72 kbit/s. An inhouse point-to-point link requires two V.35 SH units, one at each end, and the maximum separation between units is approximately 2 km. The connecting medium between units can be twisted pair cable, coaxial cable or fibre-optic cable.

Some products offer high transmission rates up to several Mbit/s over shorter distances.

All products are provided as free-standing mains powered units.

These V.35 SH products are normally used to connect computer to computer, computer to cluster controller or multiplexer to multiplexer.

SUMMARY

The following list summarises some of the many methods available for the inhouse connection of computers/terminals (devices).

Equipment Required

None	Direct connect cable (15 m) used to connect together two asynchronous devices each with a V.24/V.28 (RS-232-C) interface
Null Modem	Used with two modem interface cables (total length 15 m) to connect together two asynchronous devices each with a V.24/V.28 (RS-232-C) interface
Modem Simulator	Used with two modem interface cables (total length 15/30 m) to connect together two synchronous devices each with a V.24/V.28 (RS-232-C) interface
None	Wires only 4-wire point-to-point line (several kilometres) used to connect together two asynchronous devices each with a 20/60 mA current loop interface
Current Loop Converter	Used with wires only 4-wire point-to-point line (several kilometres) to connect together two asynchronous devices one with a current loop interface and one with a V.24/V.28 (RS-232-C) interface
Two SH units	Used with wires only 4-wire point-to-point line (several kilometres) to connect together two asynchronous or synchronous devices each with a V.24/V.28 (RS-232-C) interface
Many SH units	Used with wires only 4-wire daisy-chained line to connect one computer using poll/select protocol to a number of terminals; all with V.24/V.28 (RS-232-C) interfaces
Two Multiplexers (with integrated SH units)	Used with wires only 4-wire point-to-point line to connect many asynchronous devices (or one computer system) in one location to many asynchronous devices in another location; each with a V.24/V.28 (RS-232-C) interface

Two Conventional Multiplexers each with separate synchronous SH unit	Used with wires only 4-wire point-to-point line to connect many asynchronous devices (or one computer system) in one location to many asynchronous devices in another location; each with a V.24/V.28 (RS-232-C) interface
Two Fibre-optic SH units	Used with fibre-optic point-to-point cable to connect together two asynchronous or synchronous devices; each with a V.24/V.28 (RS-232-C) interface
Two Fibre-optic Multiplexers	Used with fibre-optic point-to-point cable to connect together many asynchronous or synchronous devices in one location to a similar number in another location; each with a V.24/V.28 (RS-232-C) interface
Data Over Voice Equipment	Used with PBX extension 2-wire lines to connect together terminals at telephone locations to a computer system or "gateway" all with V.24/V.28 (RS-232-C) interfaces

Chapter 5

Analogue Networks

LEASED TELEPHONE CIRCUITS

Introduction

Leased telephone circuits (lines) in the UK are supplied by British Telecom and are circuits which are fully dedicated to the customer's data communications operation.

There are two main types of leased circuit configuration; point-to-point circuits and multipoint circuits.

Point-to-Point Circuits

A point-to-point circuit (line) connects geographical point A to geographical point B and can be supplied as a 4-wire circuit or a 2-wire circuit. Each circuit requires two modems (one at each end) to produce a modem link (Fig. 5.1). The modems can be asynchronous or synchronous.

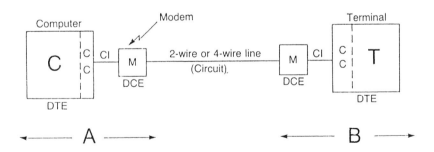

Fig. 5.1. Point-to-point circuit.

Multipoint Circuits

A multipoint circuit (single star configuration) as supplied by British Telecom consists of a main 4-wire line from the main (computer) central site to a British Telecom branching panel located in a British Telecom telephone exchange (Fig. 5.2). Four-wire lines (called spurs) radiate from the branching panel to remote (terminal) locations. It is possible to have two branching panel locations on one multipoint circuit; this is known as a double star configuration. There is a limit imposed by British Telecom of up to twelve spurs per multipoint circuit (single or double star).

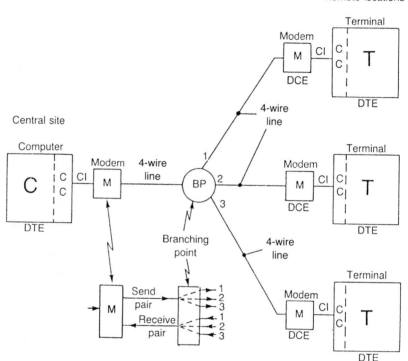

Fig. 5.2. Multipoint circuit.

One multipoint circuit requires one modem connected to the main line at the main site, and one modem connected to each spur line in each remote location. If there are N spurs (remote locations), then the number of modems required for a multipoint circuit is N+1. A multipoint circuit can use asynchronous modems (asynchronous operation) or synchronous modems (synchronous operation).

A multipoint network can also be configured from a number of point-to-point circuits by using a branching panel (British Telecom or

BABT approved) supplied by a modem manufacturer. In this case the branching panel is installed on the customer's premises and the main line and the spurs are standard 4-wire point-to-point leased lines. A true multi-drop circuit can be constructed using two way branching panels on a number of different premises all connected in series (cascaded).

Multipoint circuits are normally used for the following reasons.

They reduce line costs (annual rental).

They reduce modem costs. For example, if six remote locations are connected to a main site by six individual point-to-point circuits, then twelve modems are required. Using a multipoint circuit reduces the modem count to seven.

They reduce the maximum number (and cost) of communications hardware interfaces required by a central computer system.

Intelligent terminals are normally used on synchronous multipoint circuits with the most common type being clustered display systems. A half-duplex poll/select type of line protocol is used on multipoint lines. The main computer system is the master and controls all the data transfers between itself and the terminals (slaves).

Polling multiplexers are used on synchronous multipoint links and provide interfaces for the connection of asynchronous teletype compatible VDUs in remote locations to the asynchronous ports of a central computer system. A multiplexer at the main site has one asynchronous interface for each remote terminal. At each remote location there is an outstation multiplexer with normally one or two asynchronous interfaces for VDU attachment. The main multiplexer controls the outstation multiplexers using a poll/select type of protocol. The central computer and the asynchronous teletype compatible VDUs are not involved in any poll/select procedure (protocol). Multiplexers are discussed in Chapter 7.

Half-Duplex Operation on Multipoint Circuits

A poll "message" transmitted by the main computer (or main multiplexer) is received by all the remote outstations. This is a form of broadcast and the main computer's modem (modulator) uses continuous (constant) carrier operation over one 2-wire pair of the 4-wire multipoint circuit to all the outstation modems (demodulators). If the terminal identity contained in the poll does not match the outstation's identity then the poll is ignored. An outstation that recognises the poll responds by sending one of two types of "message"; either the first block of its data or a character sequence indicating no data to send.

An outstation must use switched carrier operation when sending its "message" by turning on "request to send" to its modem (modulator) before transmission and turning it off after transmission. If two outstations attempt to send at the same time then their modem signals will be garbled by the operation of the branching panel. A branching panel combines all the send pairs of the lines from outstation modems (modulators) into the receive pair of the line to the main computer's modem (demodulator). If an outstation fails such that its "request to send" signal is left permanently on, then the combining of line signals by the branching panel will make modulated line signals from other outstations unintelligible. An outstation modem which has its carrier permanently on is said to be "streaming". Modem Network Management Systems have the ability to "talk" to outstation modems to inhibit "streaming".

Leased Line Termination

A leased telephone line (circuit) is terminated in a customer's premises as a 2-wire termination (presentation) or a 4-wire termination. The number of wires in the British Telecom cable (local end) connecting the customer's premises to the nearest British Telecom telephone exchange corresponds to the number of wires in the presentation (i.e. a 2-wire presentation requires a 2-wire local end).

A leased telephone circuit has two local ends (one at each end) and all the other sections of the circuit which are not local ends have a 4-wire presentation. Therefore in the case of a circuit which has a 2-wire presentation, 2/4 wire conversion units (hybrid transformers) are fitted in each local telephone exchange which serves a local end.

A modem which is connected in a customer's premises to a 2-wire line, sends and receives data over the same two wires (pair). A modem connected to a 4-wire line sends data over one pair and receives data over the other pair.

Each pair of wires in a local end telephone cable passes frequencies (tones) within a given band (bandwidth). In the UK the bandwidth of an analogue telephone circuit is limited by electronic equipment within the telephone network to a range of 300–3400 Hz. These frequency limits approximately relate (on a piano) to the 'D' (293.7 Hz) one whole tone above middle 'C' and to the 'A' (3520 Hz) four octaves and a sixth above middle 'C'.

The actual wires used in the local end cable have a much wider bandwidth. For some wide-band/digital services this bandwidth supports a high speed connection (48–64 kbit/s) from a customer's premises to the local exchange.

A 4-wire termination (presentation) has twice the available bandwidth of a 2-wire termination. Modems which provide only synchronous operation (as compared to asynchronous/synchronous modems) and operate from 2400 bit/s to 19,200 bit/s always require a 4-wire line presentation when they are connected to leased telephone lines.

Grades of Leased Telephone Line

There are different qualities (grades) of line and the cost of renting a leased line increases with quality. Modem manufacturers know the quality of line required for correct operation of their products and this should be established prior to selection.

In the UK the grades of leased line are complicated by the changes in grading and terminology introduced by British Telecom over the years.

Before 1979, British Telecom specified its leased lines by tariff and there were four tariffs, known as Tariff S1, Tariff S2, Tariff S3 and Tariff T.

These were well-established tariffs and people still identify lines by them. In discussing the changes these tariffs will be used for comparison purposes.

Between 1979 and 1983 British Telecom defined four grades of British Telecom leased telephone line which were specified in terms of Schedule A, B, C and D. In simple terms Schedule D was the best grade of line and the most expensive, and Schedule A the worst grade and the least expensive. Schedule D was roughly equivalent to Tariff T and Schedule A to Tariff S1. As a guide, Schedule C or Schedule D 4-wire lines were required for 9600 bit/s synchronous only modems. The following table shows leased line configurations using these schedules.

British Telecom Schedule	Termination (Presentation)	
	Point-to-Point	Multipoint
A	2-wire only	Not available
B	2-wire or 4-wire	4-wire only
C	2-wire or 4-wire	Not available
D	2-wire or 4-wire	4-wire only

Since early 1983 British Telecom has introduced a new tariff structure for leased (private) circuits called A-Line Services. Lines which are used for speech are known as Speechline circuits and those used for data transmission (with modems) are known as Keyline circuits. The new tariff structure for A-Line Services is divided for charging purposes into Analogue A and Analogue B circuits. Analogue A is equivalent to the old Tariff S1 and Tariff S2 and Analogue B is equivalent to the old Tariff S3, Tariff T and multipoint circuits.

UK Leased Line Costs

Leased line costs consist of a one-time connection charge and an annual rental. Under the new A-Line tariff structure, the annual rental of a leased (private) circuit is divided into two separate chargeable elements. The link (local end) from a customer's site to its Serving Exchange has a fixed charge which is not distance related. The charge for the link between Serving Exchanges is related to the radial distance between the two exchanges. Remember that each point-to-point leased circuit has two local ends.

Actual line costs have not been shown because they are revised at frequent intervals. To determine the cost of a leased line in the UK, contact the nearest local Telephone Manager's office and ask for the phone number of Datel Services.

UK WIDE-BAND ANALOGUE CIRCUITS

A wide-band circuit is a leased point-to-point full-duplex analogue circuit and provides a bandwidth of from 60 kHz to 108 kHz between telephone exchanges. This 48 kHz of bandwidth is equivalent to that used by a group of twelve telephone circuits. Wide-band modems, sometimes known as group-band modems, use this bandwidth to send/receive data at transmission rates from 48 kbit/s to 168 kbit/s.

There are three CCITT recommendations associated with wide-band operation and these are:

> V.35 recommendation
> Data transmission at 48 kbits/s using 60–108 kHz group band circuits.

> V.36 recommendation
> Modems for synchronous data transmission using 60–108 kHz group band circuits.

> V.37 recommendation
> Synchronous data transmission at a data signalling rate higher than 72 kbits/s using 60–108 kHz group band circuits.

V.35 specifies the wide-band electrical interface and modem operation at a transmission rate of 48 kbit/s. V.36 specifies modem operation at transmission rates from 48 kbit/s to 72 kbit/s and V.37 specifies modem operation for transmission rates from 96 kbit/s to 168 kbit/s.

British Telecom provides a Datel 48K service which uses four modems; two modems at each end of a wide-band circuit. One of the two modems is in the telephone exchange (repeater station) and the other is on the customer's premises and they are connected together by a 4-wire local line (Fig. 5.3).

The Datel 48K service initially used the Datel modems Nos 8 and 9 but now offers the Datel modems Nos 35 and 36.

Customer's premises	Telephone exchange	CCITT Rec.	Transmission rate in kbit/s
Modem No. 8	Modem No. 9	V.35	48
Modem No. 35	Modem No. 36	V.36	48, 60, 64, 72

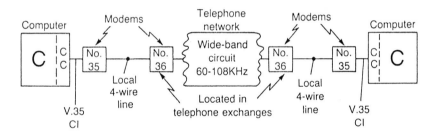

Fig. 5.3. Datel 48K Wide-band link.

In the UK some manufacturers provide V.37 modems which operate at 96–168 kbit/s over a wide-band circuit. Two modems are normally required per link, one at each end.

AMERICAN LEASED ANALOGUE LINES

Telephone Type Lines

The basic unconditioned 4-wire line in the USA is the Bell 3002 voice-grade circuit and is the most commonly used data circuit. This basic circuit can be provided, at additional cost, with improved characteristics by the incorporation of C or D conditioning.

There are five types of C conditioning, known as C1, C2, C3, C4 and C5, and these are used to overcome amplitude distortion and envelope delay distortion.

There are two types of D conditioning, known as D1 and D2, and these are used to overcome noise (C-notched) and harmonic distortion on point-to-point and multipoint circuits respectively.

Wide-band Lines

Wide-band lines (circuits) in the USA are provided by the Bell Series 8000 wide-band service which operates at 19.2, 40.8 and 50 kbit/s.

NETWORKS THAT USE ANALOGUE CIRCUITS

Analogue circuits can be used in many different ways in the construction of networks; the following are a few examples.

A network can be constructed using only analogue circuits, modems and a suitable communications protocol. These types of networks are discussed in Chapter 16.

A network can be constructed using frequency division multiplexers and telephone type analogue circuits (no modems required). Similarly a network can be constructed using time division multiplexers, analogue circuits and synchronous modems. Multiplexer networks are discussed in Chapter 7.

British Telecom's PSS X.25 network uses analogue links called "Datalines" to connect computers, terminals and Packet Assembler/Disassemblers (PADs) to their network (see Chapter 8).

Facsimile equipment on two sites can be connected by point-to-point analogue circuits (FAX Groups 1/2) or analogue links (FAX Groups 3/4).

Private Branch Exchanges (known as PABX, PBX or CBX) located on different sites can be connected by tie lines using analogue circuits (BT Speechline not Keyline services).

SWITCHED TELEPHONE CIRCUITS

The CCITT in its standards refers to public networks that provide switched telephone (analogue) circuits as the "general switched telephone network". In the UK the network provided by British Telecom is known as the Public Switched Telephone Network (PSTN).

The PSTN is the network used by the public for ordinary telephone conversations. It is also a network that is used for data communication operations particularly when a connection between two geographical points is required for only a few minutes or hours per day.

In the USA the switched telephone network is known as the DDD (Direct Distance Dial) network and modem connection is permitted using a DAA (Data Access Arrangement).

UK Connection Charges

The PSTN connection charges for data communication operations are the same as for normal telephone use. (There is one exception in the UK called the Midnight Line Service which is discussed later.)

For each user there is a cost break-point where the annual charges for PSTN connect time between geographical point A and geographical point B exceed the annual rental of a leased (dedicated) line. A user should calculate this cost break-point using the latest telephone charges.

On new data communication systems, there is often no alternative to PSTN connection in the first few months of operation because British Telecom usually takes some time to install new leased circuits. This fact should be considered when modem configurations are being designed.

Direct Exchange Line

The line between a customer's premises and the nearest PSTN exchange is known as a Direct Exchange Line (DEL) and this line has a 2-wire presentation. All connections through the PSTN are point-to-point 2-wire connections: geographical point A can make a connection to geographical point B. If A is now to be connected to geographical point C then the first connection must be broken down and a new point-to-point connection established.

Auto-Call Operation

The manual method of establishing a data communications link through the PSTN is by a person at point A manually dialling the telephone number of point B. The person at point B answers the call by lifting the telephone handset from the telephone and a PSTN connection between point A and point B is established. After speaking to verify that the correct connection has been made, both persons (at A and B) operate the "data" buttons on their telephones (or modems) to switch their modems on to the PSTN line.

Instead of manually dialling the connection for a data communications link, a computer can be used to dial-up its own connections. This is known as Auto-Call (Dial) operation and until recently required special software and equipment at the computer end. The equipment consisted of a special computer interface (V.25 Auto-Call Interface) and a free-standing Auto-Call Unit connected as shown in Fig. 2.4 (Chapter 2).

In the UK the Auto-Call Unit (ACU) provided for over ten years by British Telecom was called 'Data Control Equipment No. 1A' abbreviated to DCE1A. The DCE1A was replaced by the Datel Autocaller. In the USA the ACU is the Bell 801 ACU.

The ACU situation has changed with the introduction of modems with auto-call capability. A computer connected to one of these modems uses only one V.24/V.28 (RS-232-C) interface to perform both auto-call and data transfer operations.

The first auto-calling modems were asynchronous and used the modem manufacturer's own procedure for auto-calling.

The new V.25 bis recommendation (when approved) will standardise the auto-call procedure for asynchronous/synchronous modems with auto-calling capability.

Some synchronous modems incorporate automatic calling circuitry which they themselves use to dial two PSTN connections (double dial-up) for standby PSTN operation. This procedure is initiated when a modem detects that its leased line has failed; this operation is known as auto-restoral.

An auto-dialled call initiated from point A is usually automatically answered by the equipment at point B.

Auto-Answer Operation

A computer, intelligent terminal, intelligent modem or dial back-up unit can automatically answer a manually dialled or auto-dialled call; this is known as auto-answer operation.

Auto-answering of "manually" dialled calls is normally performed by the following equipments.

> A time-sharing system using a mainframe computer or a mini-computer normally auto-answers calls from remote terminal users.

> Special purpose modem ancillary equipment (dial back-up unit) is located at a remote modem location to answer automatically one or more dialled calls from a computer centre. In the event of a leased line failure it establishes a temporary (standby) circuit using one or more PSTN connections to restore a modem link.

Auto-answering of "automatically" dialled calls is normally performed by intelligent terminals or modem equipment. For example, one use of this type of auto-answer operation is for the collection (after each working day) of data from unattended Point of Sale (POS) terminals.

The hardware required is a standard modem configured for auto-answer operation and a V.24/V.28 (RS-232-C) communications hardware interface (CHI) forming part of a DTE (terminal). The CHI provides a path between the modem's interchange circuits and auto-answer software running on the processor unit of the terminal.

The four modem interchange circuits which can be used by auto-answer software are:

Interchange Circuit	Modem Pin No.	Description
107	6	Data Set Ready [DSR]
109	8	Received Line Signal Detector (Carrier Detect) [CD]
108/1 108/2	20	Connect Data Set to line [CDSTL] or Data Terminal Ready [DTR]
125	22	Calling (Ringing) Indicator [RI]

Of these four signals, only circuit 107 (pin 6) DSR and circuit 108 (pin 20) CDSTL/DTR are normally required for auto-answer operation.

CDSTL/DTR Auto-Answer Operation

The CDSTL/DTR modem interchange circuit 108 (pin 20) is controlled by a DTE (terminal) connected to a modem. A modem is set up by internal straps/switches or by software to support either CDSTL or DTR auto-answer operation on interchange circuit 108 (pin 20).

With "data terminal ready" (DTR) operation, when auto-answer operation is required, a computer/terminal (DTE) puts on DTR (pin 20). When a modem connected to the DTE receives a dialled call, it detects the ringing. If DTR is on, the modem automatically answers the call and connects itself to the line. This is indicated to the DTE by "data set ready" (pin 6) changing state from off (−V) to on (+V). The exchange of modem carriers between the two modems causes "carrier detect" (pin 8) to change state from off to on.

Data transmission can now take place between the two DTEs on either end of the PSTN modem link.

To disconnect the PSTN link the DTE puts off DTR (pin 20). The

DTE will put DTR on again if further auto-answer operation is required. In practice DTE is taken to the off state for only 200 ms which is sufficient to allow the telephone exchange to clear down.

With "connect dataset to line" (CDSTL) operation a DTE keeps CDSTL (pin 20) in the off (−V) state. When a modem connected to a DTE receives a dialled call it switches its "calling indicator" (pin 22) on and off in sympathy with the ringing signal. The DTE (software) detects the first transition from off to on of the "calling indicator" interchange circuit 125 (pin 22) and puts on CDSTL (pin 20) to answer the call and connect the modem to line. From this point on, operation is similar to "data terminal ready" operation except for the PSTN disconnect sequence. When the PSTN link is to be disconnected the DTE puts off CDSTL (pin 20).

In the UK, DTR operation is more widely used than CDSTL operation.

Phases In Auto-Answering

There are a number of phases in auto-answering:

Ready to receive a dialled call (known in the USA as being "on hook");

Answering a dialled call and establishing a PSTN connection which is equivalent to lifting the telephone handset from the telephone (known in the USA as going from the "on hook" condition to the "off hook" condition);

Establishing by data exchange the identity of the answering device;

Sending/receiving data over the PSTN connection;

Disconnecting the PSTN connection which is equivalent to replacing the handset on the telephone (going from "off hook" to "on hook").

Midnight Line Service

This British Telecom service allows a customer to make unlimited use of the PSTN between the hours of midnight and 6 a.m. daily for a fixed annual rental per direct exchange line. To implement this service British Telecom installs additional equipment (in a telephone exchange) which disables the normal telephone metering during the hours of the midnight line service. This service was specifically introduced for auto-call operation and is normally used on computer centre direct exchange lines.

Services Accessed via the PSTN

In the UK there are many services that can be accessed via the PSTN. The following is a cross-section:

Data networks private and public (e.g. BT's PSS, Euronet Diane);

Electronic Mail services, including BT's Telecom Gold;

Viewdata services, including BT's Prestel service;

The Teletex service for document transfer;

BT's Bureaufax service for the collection/distribution (world-wide) of documents between incompatible facsimile machines;

Voice messaging services.

Summary of Modems for Use on the PSTN

In the following tables no distinction has been made between modems dedicated to PSTN operation and those connected to the PSTN for standby operation.

When a leased line fails on a modem link the PSTN is often used to provide a short term (hours or days) standby (back-up) circuit as a temporary replacement.

Asynchronous Modems for use on a single dialled connection

Transmission Rate in bit/s	V Rec.	Type of Operation	Modem
300	V.21	FDX	Datel 200 modem [2]* or [13]* or [21]*
300	V.21	FDX	Datel modem 413X
600 or 1200 or 75/1200	V.23 V.23	HDX FDX	Datel 600 modem [1]* or [20]* or [22]*
300 or 75/1200 or 600 or 1200	V.21 V.23 V.23	FDX FDX HDX	Datel modem 4123 or Datelphone 4123
300 or 1200	V.21 V.22	FDX FDX	Datel modem 4124
1200		FDX	Datel 1200 Duplex modem [27]*
1200 or 600	V.22	FDX	Datel modem 4122 or Datelphone 4122
1200 or 2400	V.22 V.22 bis	FDX FDX	Datel modem 4242
300 or 600 or 1200 75/1200 1200 2400 bit/s 4800 bit/s	V.21 V.23 V.23 V.22 V.22 bis	FDX HDX FDX FDX FDX FDX	Various modems offered by many manufacturers

Synchronous Modems for use on a single dialled connection

Transmission rate in bit/s	V Rec.	Type of operation	Modem
600 or 1200		HDX	Datel 2400 modem [7]*
1200	V.22	FDX	Datel 1200 Duplex modem [27]*
1200	V.22	FDX	Datel modem 4124
1200	V.22	FDX	Datel modem 4122 or Datelphone 4122
600 or 1200 or 2400		HDX	Datel 2400 Dial-up modem [7C]*
1200 or 2400		HDX	Datel 2412 modem [12]*
1200 or 2400	V.26 V.26 bis	HDX	Datel modem 4241 or Datelphone 4241
1200 or 2400	V.22 V.22 bis	FDX FDX	Datel modem 4242
2400 or 4800		HDX	Datel 4800 modem [11]*
2400 or 4800	V.27 bis V.27 ter	HDX	Datel modem 4480
4800 or 4800 or 7200	V.27 V.29	HDX	Datel modem 4960
4800 or 9600	V.32	FDX	Datel modem 4962
1200–4800 2400–9600		FDX } HDX }	Various modems offered by many manufacturers

Synchronous Modems for use on two dialled connections "Double Dial-Up"

Transmission rate in bit/s	V Rec.	Type of operation	Modem
2400 or 4800	V.27 bis V.27 ter	FDX	Datel modem 4480
3200 or 4800		FDX	Datel 4832 modem [24]*
4800 or 9600		FDX	Datel 9600 modem [30]*
4800 or 4800 or 7200 or 9600	V.27 V.29 V.29	FDX	Datel modem 4960
4800 or 9600		FDX	Datel modem 4961
2400–9600		FDX	Various modems offered by many manufacturers

British Telecom Datel modems are shown as examples of the types of modem used with the UK PSTN. The model numbers of Datel modems are shown in brackets; those marked with an asterisk have been superseded but are included because some are still in service. A Datelphone is a modem plus a telephone (with repertory dialler) packaged as one unit and used in outstation locations.

Note: BT is now adding a suffix "X" to 4000 series modems which have been BABT approved ("X" is not shown in the tables).

Chapter 6

Digital Networks

A BRIEF HISTORY OF DIGITAL TRANSMISSION

The first digital transmission equipment was introduced in the early 1960s by PTTs into their telephone networks to increase the carrying capacity of cable pairs used on short distance routes between telephone exchanges.

This equipment used pulse code modulation (PCM) and provided 24 voice channels over one 4-wire line.

The UK and North America adopted different incompatible encoding standards for their PCM systems known as A-law and mu-law respectively and these two encoding methods eventually became CCITT recommended standards. In both standards each individual channel operates at 64,000 bits per second (64 kbit/s).

European administrations finally standardised on a 30-channel design operating at 2048 kbit/s using A-law and North America on a 24-channel (Bell T-1) design operating at 1544 kbit/s using mu-law. Japan adopted the North American standard.

For transmission over high speed bearer links, these standard transmission rates are multiplexed up to higher rates and the transmission medium normally used is either coaxial cable, fibre-optic cable or microwave.

The multiplexing up of these basic digital transmission rates has produced the following hierarchy with a divergence between North America and Japan at Level 3. This divergence is to satisfy their different network requirements.

Hierarchy level	Europe	Japan	North America
	64 kbit/s	64 kbit/s	64 kbit/s
1	2,048 kbit/s	1,544 kbit/s	1,544 kbit/s
2	8,448 kbit/s	6,312 kbit/s	6,312 kbit/s
3	34,368 kbit/s	32,064 kbit/s	44,736 kbit/s
4	139,264 kbit/s	97,728 kbit/s	274,176 kbit/s
5		397,200 kbit/s	

These transmission rates are usually referred to in terms of megabits per second (Mbit/s) and rounded to a whole number (e.g. 2 Mbit/s, 8 Mbit/s, 32 Mbit/s, 34 Mbit/s, 45 Mbit/s, 140 Mbit/s, and 400 Mbit/s).

Appendix G list the CCITT G.700 Recommendations for Digital Networks.

UK DIGITAL SERVICES

British Telecom and Mercury Communications both offer a range of communications services based on the use of digital networks.

British Telecom Digital Services

The services offered by British Telecom are known as X-Stream Digital Services. A brief description of these services follows.

Kilostream

This digital service provides full-duplex synchronous point-to-point links at 2400 bit/s, 4800 bit/s, 9600 bit/s, 48 kbit/s, and 64 kbit/s. It is available between approximately 200 telephone exchange areas throughout the UK. The customer interface to Kilostream is via a Network Termination Unit (NTU) installed on the customer's premises. An NTU physically resembles a modem and is connected to a local Kilostream exchange by a 4-wire local circuit. An NTU transmits and receives digital signals over a 4-wire local circuit at 12.8 kbit/s or 64 kbit/s using Walsh 2 (WAL2) diphase transmission. The customer's computer/terminal interface to an NTU is CCITT X.21 or X.21 bis.

The Kilostream X.21 interface operates at 2400 bit/s, 4800 bit/s, 9600 bit/s, 48 kbit/s or 64 kbit/s.

The Kilostream X.21 bis interface provides V.24/V.28 (RS-232-C) compatibility at 2400 bit/s, 4800 bit/s, or 9600 bit/s and V.35 compatibility at 48 kbit/s.

The Kilostream network comprises 2 Mbit/s links connecting multiplexers at nominated serving exchanges via cross-connect sites (see Fig. 6.1).

The equipment at a cross-connect site takes in a number of 2 Mbit/s signal streams and demultiplexes them into individual 64 kbit/s time-slots which are then routed to the required 64 kbit/s time-slots in the appropriate outgoing 2 Mbit/s signal streams. The equipment is microprocessor controlled and the routing can be controlled from a VDU either locally or remotely from a network control centre. The network is monitored by two Network Control Centres located at Manchester and London. At transmission rates up to and including 48 kbit/s an NTU adds two extra bits (alignment bit and status bit) to each 6 bits transmitted by a user. These two bits are used for control and in-service monitoring purposes by network control. At transmission rates of 64 kbit/s these two bits are required for data and therefore monitoring of a circuit right up to the NTU (in-service monitoring) is not possible.

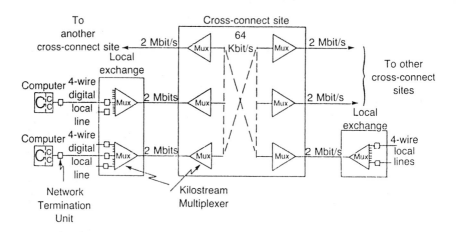

Fig. 6.1. Kilostream cross-connect site.

Megastream

This digital leased line service provides point-to-point synchronous 2048 kbit/s (2 Mbits/s) links which can be directly connected to a modern PBX for voice transmission or can be used for very high speed data transmission. Megastream also provides even higher speed point-to-point links of 8 Mbit/s, 34 Mbit/s or 144 Mbit/s.

A variety of time division multiplexers (TDMs) are available for use on Megastream links. A TDM connected at each end of a 2 Mbit/s Megastream link can provide a number of different multiplexer channel options:

> 30 analogue 2/4-wire channels, each channel can be used for analogue speech or for data transmission using modems at data rates up to 9600 bit/s;

A total of 30 analogue 2/4-wire channels and/or digital 64 kbit/s channels (X.21);

Up to 64 synchronous or 54 asynchronous/synchronous data channels (V.24/V.28, V.10, V.11, V.35) and optionally a number of 32/64 kbit/s digital speech channels.

International Kilostream-Megastream

Before this service was introduced, British Telecom International (BTI) used analogue circuits to connect users to its satellite earth stations. BTI then linked the inland Kilostream and Megastream networks to its satellite earth stations enabling users to have digital access to international services.

For a typical International Kilostream circuit a Network Terminating Unit (NTU) is located in the customer's UK premises connected by a 4-wire local line to a nearby Kilostream exchange. From the exchange the circuit is connected via BT's trunk network to the international gateway in London. At the gateway the circuit is carried by satellite link, cable or microwave system to its international destination.

International Kilostream provides synchronous full-duplex data transmission at 1200 bit/s, 2400 bit/s, 4800 bit/s, 9600 bit/s or 56 kbit/s using an X.21 bis interface (V.24 or V.35).

International Megastream provides synchronous full-duplex data transmission at 2.048 Mbit/s to CCITT standard G.732. Additional equipment can convert this to 1.544 Mbit/s G.733 operation for North America. This rate is often referred to as 2/1.5 Mbit/s.

For a typical International Megastream circuit, Line Terminating Equipment (LTE) is located in the customer's premises connected by a special cable to the nearest digital exchange. From there the circuit is routed to the international gateway and onward to the distant network using similar transmission methods to International Kilostream.

BTI provides a "time assigned service" at 56 kbit/s (Kilostream) and 2/1.5 Mbit/s (Megastream) which offers a pre-bookable link between the UK and distant end international gateways. For this service a full time digital link to the UK international gateway is required which incurs connection and annual rental charges.

Satstream

This is a British Telecom International Service which uses small-dish (3.7 to 5.5 m diameter) satellite earth stations ("terminals") to provide digital links between the UK, Europe and North America. The service provides one-way or both-way point-to-point (or point to multipoint) digital links which operate at 64 kbit/s or selected multiples of 64 kbit/s up to 1920 kbit/s. Multiplexer options are available for lower bit rates, and the service can be provided on a full time, regular part time or *ad hoc* basis.

British Telecom "terminals" are sited in a number of fixed locations in the UK and Satstream is provided as a dedicated link from a "terminal" to a customer's site. Alternatively, where there is a need, British Telecom can install on the customer's site a fixed "terminal" or a transportable "terminal" mounted on a trailer.

Videostream

This is a video-conferencing service which offers full-motion monochrome (black and white) or colour video-conferencing between a customer's premises. Equipment is supplied for installation in conference rooms and offices. One of the main items of equipment is a CODEC (coder-decoder) which converts a black and white or colour video signal into a 2 Mbits/s digital signal for transmission over Megastream or an equivalent bandwidth link. Other items include TV cameras, television type monitors, loudspeakers, etc.

There are two other associated British Telecom services.

Confravision is similar to Videostream except that equipment is located in a number of British Telecom studios. The studios are booked by telephone and charged for by the half hour.

The International Video-conferencing service provides a video-conferencing link between a British Telecom studio in London and studio locations in North America, Canada or Europe. A gateway will be provided to allow Videostream custom rs to access International Video-conferencing locations.

Switchstream

Packet Switchstream (PSS) is British Telecom's X.25 packet switched data service. The international extension of PSS is called International PSS and provides an X.25 gateway to X.25 services in other countries.

Interstream is an associated PSS service which provides a gateway between PSS, the UK PSTN and UK Telex/Teletex Services.

PSS and Interstream are described in Chapter 8.

Mercury Communications

Mercury Communications is an independent organisation operating under a licence granted in February 1982 from the British Government as a second telecommunications carrier in Great Britain and overseas. At its formation the company was jointly owned by Cable and Wireless plc, the British Petroleum Company plc and Barclays Merchant Bank Ltd., but since August 1984 the company has been exclusively owned by Cable and Wireless plc.

Mercury intends to offer its business customers a leased line service to be followed by switched services. The leased line service is organised in "unit circuits" of 64 kbit/s and employs time division multiplexing. Data is presented to a user as one or more 64 kbit/s or 2 Mbit/s circuits which can be sub-divided into a mix of voice and/or data streams or combined to provide very high speed high capacity links. At the upper end, Mercury provides circuits of 8, 34, 68 and 140 Mbit/s.

Leased line services at 64 kbit/s and 2 Mbit/s are made by cross-connection of circuits and time slots at nodes and trunk access points.

A 64 kbit/s circuit can be supplied in any one of the following configurations:

One 64 kbit/s PCM voice circuit;

Two 32 kbit/s Continuously Variable Slope Delta (CVSD) modulation voice circuits, each supporting voice band data up to 1200 bit/s;

One 32 kbit/s CVSD voice circuit supporting voice band data up to 1200 bit/s, plus a mix of data circuits up to an aggregate of 31 kbit/s;

Up to 54 data channels with a total aggregate rate of 64 kbit/s providing asynchronous data rates from 50 to 9600 bit/s and/or synchronous data rates from 150 to 57,600 bit/s (V.24/V.28, V.10, V.11, V.35).

A 2 Mbit/s circuit can be supplied in any one of the following configurations:

Thirty 64 kbit/s PCM voice circuits;

Thirty 64 kbit/s PCM voice/data mix circuits;

Sixty 32 kbit/s Adaptive Differential Pulse Code Modulation (ADPCM) voice circuits each supporting voice band data up to 4800 bit/s;

Up to 54 CVSD voice/data mix channels with a total aggregate of 2 Mbit/s providing a mix of asynchronous data up to 9600 bit/s, synchronous data up to 1.544 Mbit/s (V.24/V.28, V.10, V.11, V.35, Bell T-1) and CVSD modulated voice.

Connection of Users

In the long term, customers will be connected by cable either as a dedicated line, part of a cable television network or part of a wide area network.

The initial method adopted by Mercury to connect a customer is to use digital radio (microwave) links transmitting/receiving in the 10.5 and 13 GHz bands. This has the advantage of being relatively quick to install but requires a line of sight path between a customer's site and a Mercury node.

Low capacity connections (64 kbit/s) are provided by a 10.5 GHz cellular radio system whereby the urban area to be covered is divided into a number of cells of similar diameter. Each cell is divided into 3/4 segments (sectors) which are 90–120° wide. A Mercury node at or near the centre of each cell communicates with customer sites within that cell via a number of fan shaped microwave beams, one beam per segment. Each customer site communicates with its node via a narrow "pencil" microwave beam produced by a small (60 cm diameter) parabolic reflector antenna installed on the customer's premises. A different set of frequencies within the 10.5 GHz band is used in each segment (sector). The frequency sets are arranged with alternate polarisations to protect against interference from other cells.

Within a sector, a Mercury node transmits traffic at 2 Mbits/s using a form of broadcast transmission to all customer sites in its sector. The transmitted traffic is time division multiplexed and a preamble at the start of each TDM frame contains address information which is used by a customer's receiver to extract its own traffic. The preamble also contains "start of burst" timing information which is used by a customer's transmitter to initiate a traffic burst and so prevent all the transmitters in the sector from sending at the same time. A transmitter at a customer's location transmits to its node using time division multiple access (TDMA) on a separate return carrier. A node transmits to a sector at 2 Mbit/s and can support up to thirty 64 kbit/s circuits. These can be assigned to one customer location or assigned to up to 30 separate locations in the sector.

A node that operates with four sectors can support an aggregate data rate of 8 Mbit/s (2 Mbit/s per sector).

This local distribution at 64 kbit/s is called digital multipoint radio and has a range from node to customer location of up to 10 km.

Customers requiring a 2 Mbit/s or higher point-to-point service, are connected by dedicated 13 GHz microwave (digital radio) systems with a range of 25 km to a Mercury node or direct to the other location.

Local distribution nodes are connected to central trunk distribution nodes by 13 GHz microwave systems operating at a data rate of 8 Mbit/s or 34 Mbit/s.

The Mercury Network

The Mercury network started in the UK in the City and West End of London with an intra-city service based on microwave radio links. Mercury nodes are sited at the following locations in London:

Willesden Tower
Melbury House, Marylebone
Britannic House, Moorgate
Guys Tower, Southwark
Millbank.

The intra-city service has been expanded to an inter-city trunk network where London, Birmingham and Manchester are connected by 13 GHz micro-wave links operating at 34 Mbit/s.

This micro-wave trunk network is to be supplemented (and eventually replaced) by the main Mercury optical fibre trunk network (see Fig. 6.2).

The optical fibre trunk network is a geographic "figure of eight" network linking major commercial centres and individual towns with Birmingham (National Control Centre) situated at the centre of the two loops. The southern loop of the network includes London and Bristol and the northern loop includes Leeds and Manchester. Under an agreement signed with British Rail, the optical fibre cables will be laid in concrete troughs located at the side of railway tracks. Monomode optical fibre cables will be used with regenerators (repeaters) spaced at an average distance of 25 km. Each cable has ten fibres and each fibre will initially support a transmission rate of 140 Mbit/s, but will support a higher rate of 560 Mbit/s if the network needs to be expanded.

Each town or city on the fibre trunk network will have a trunk access node (TAN). At a TAN the optical fibre cable equipment will interface at 140 Mbit/s with digital multiplexer equipment. This equipment will multiplex/demultiplex 140 Mbit/s signals as required to/from 34 Mbit/s, 8 Mbit/s, 2 Mbit/s and 64 Kbit/s. Micro-wave links or cables will carry traffic at the required rates from a TAN via distribution nodes to customers.

International satellite links to the USA are to be supported by Mercury satellite communications centres, one located at East Wood Wharf, London and the other at Whitehill, Oxfordshire (standard C Intelsat station).

Fig. 6.2. Mercury Network.

USA DIGITAL SERVICES

The digital services provided by AT&T are known as Dataphone Digital Services (DDS) and provide data transmission rates of 2400 bit/s, 4800 bit/s, 9600 bit/s and 56 kbit/s. One of the drawbacks of this service is the lack of a basic end to end diagnostic capability. This is to be improved with the introduction of a new service known as DDS-2. This service will provide secondary channels which will allow users to run their own end to end diagnostics. The proposed DDS-2 secondary channels rates are as follows:

Data channel	Secondary channel	Total aggregate
2400 bit/s	133 bit/s	3200 bit/s
4800 bit/s	266 bit/s	6400 bit/s
9600 bit/s	533 bit/s	12800 bit/s
56 kbit/s	2666 bit/s	72 kbit/s

Every 8-bits (octet) transmitted or received over a DDS circuit consists of 6 bits of user data and 2 bits for AT&T framing/control functions.

With DDS-2, at data transmission rates of 2400, 4800 and 9600 bit/s the secondary channel will be derived by using one of the two AT&T bits in every third octet.

At 56 kbit/s, 9 bits will be used instead of 8 bits, and the 2666 bit/s secondary channel will be derived by using the ninth bit in every third 9-bit byte.

INTEGRATED DIGITAL NETWORK (IDN)

In countries throughout the world, digital transmission and digital switching equipments are gradually replacing analogue transmission and analogue switching equipments. The impact has been strongly felt in domestic telephone networks and in the UK System X digital exchanges are replacing Strowger exchanges.

From the growth of digital transmission and switching, CCITT standards have evolved for an Integrated Digital Network (IDN) in which the switching units are linked by digital transmission paths providing a 64 kbit/s switched digital network between local exchanges. For a telephony IDN, a telephone user connects to the network by a conventional 2-wire analogue line. However if the telephony IDN is extended to the customer's premises by digital transmission links with enhanced customer to network signalling, then an all-purpose network can be created. This conceptual network is known as an Integrated Services Digital Network (ISDN).

THE INTEGRATED SERVICES DIGITAL NETWORK (ISDN)

This is a new network concept which has evolved from the present Integrated Digital Network (IDN). It is being developed nationally and internationally and ISDN recommendations (I-Series) are being produced by CCITT Study Groups. The majority of the ISDN (I-Series) CCITT recommendations are still in draft form (see Appendix D). They are liable to change and this should be borne in mind when reading this ISDN description.

The concept of an ISDN is to provide a network where the same digital switches and paths are used to establish connections for a wide range of services both analogue (voice) and digital (data). For users who require access to a wide range of services the ISDN will be a natural successor in the UK to the PSTN.

Interworking between ISDN and the following Networks/Services is being considered. This is a general world-wide list and ignores national variations.

Public Switched Telephone Network (PSTN)

Circuit-Switched Public Data Network (CSPDN)

Packet Switched Public Data Network (PSPDN)

Domestic Satellite System

Leased digital lines

Leased analogue lines

Switched private networks for PBX

Telex Network

Teletex Network

Videotex Communication

Facsimile Communication

This list is summarised in the CCITT basic architectural model of an ISDN, shown in Fig. 6.3.

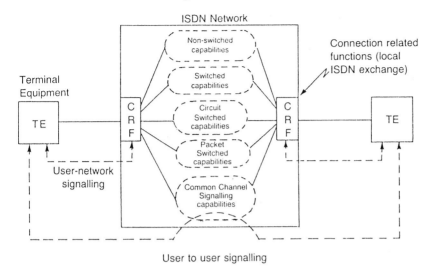

Fig. 6.3. Basic ISDN architectural model.

ISDN Reference Configuration

The CCITT has produced reference configurations for the interface point to an ISDN network (Fig. 6.4).

These reference configurations are conceptual configurations which are useful in identifying the various methods of connecting to an ISDN. Two concepts are used to describe these configurations.

The first concept is one of functional groupings which describe the set of functions which may be required in ISDN arrangements. The specific functions in a functional grouping may be performed by one or more pieces of equipment.

The second concept is one of reference points which are given alphabetic letters (R, S, T, V). These are the conceptual points at the conjunction of two functional groupings. The reference points may correspond to a physical interface between pieces of equipment or there may not be a corresponding interface.

Each box represents a functional grouping.

LT (Line Termination);

NT1 (Network Termination 1) includes functions associated with

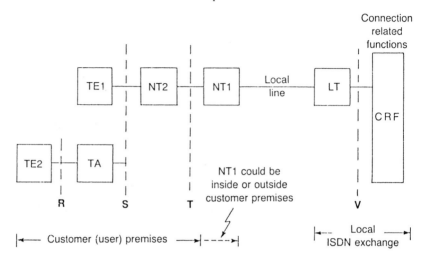

Fig. 6.4. ISDN reference configuration..

the physical and electrical termination of the network (i.e. equivalent to Open System Interconnection [OSI] layer 1);

NT2 (Network Termination 2) includes intelligent functions (i.e. equivalent to OSI layers 1, 2 and 3). Typical examples of NT2 devices are:

> Private Branch Exchange (PBX) sometimes called Private Automatic Branch Exchange (PABX) or Computerised Branch Exchange (CBX),
>
> Data Terminal Controller,
>
> Local Area Network;

TE1 (Terminal Equipment 1) is terminal equipment with an interface that complies with the ISDN user-network interface recommendation (e.g. digital telephone);

TA (Terminal Adapter);

TE2 (Terminal Equipment 2) is terminal equipment with an interface (e.g. CCITT V or X series) that requires a terminal adapter to be compatible with the ISDN user-network interface recommendation (e.g. data terminal with V.24/V.28 (RS-232-C) interface).

ISDN Interface Structures

Two different interface structures are being defined for the ISDN user-network interface.

The first is the "basic interface" structure which operates at 144 kbit/s and supports two "B" channels each operating at 64 kbit/s and one "D" channel operating at 16 kbit/s. The "B" channels are used for data transmission and the "D" channel is used for signalling and low-rate data.

The second is the "primary rate" interface which operates at 2048 kbit/s or 1544 kbit/s. At 2048 kbit/s it supports 30 "B" channels and one "D" channel, and at 1544 kbit/s it supports 23 "B" channels and one "D" channel; all channels operate at 64 kbit/s. The primary rate interface is intended for PBX connection.

INTEGRATED DIGITAL ACCESS (IDA)

British Telecom is offering a Public Network using System X digital switching and transmission which is the basis of an Integrated Services Digital Network (ISDN) carrying speech and data in digital form.

To access the ISDN, British Telecom provides an Integrated Digital Access (IDA) service from customers' premises which combines speech and data transmission over a single digital link. This link is being provided in two forms as a Single Line IDA or a Multi-line IDA.

Single Line IDA

A single line IDA provides a customer with two digital channels, each with its own network address and therefore capable of independent operation. In the initial IDA pilot phase, a single line IDA is terminated in the customer's premises on one of two Network Terminating Equipments called NTE1 and NTE3.

An NTE communicates at 80 kbit/s using full-duplex operation over an ordinary 2-wire line to a System X ISDN Exchange. The 80 kbit/s serial stream is demultiplexed inside the NTE into a 64 kbit/s data/speech channel, an 8 kbit/s data channel and an 8 kbit/s signalling channel. The 8 kbit/s and the 64 kbit/s channels can be independently routed to separate destinations under the control of the 8 kbit/s signalling channel. The signalling channel uses a protocol based on HDLC.

Network Terminating Equipment No. 1 (NTE1)

An NTE1 provides two channels of communication:

A primary (B) channel which operates synchronously at transmission rates up to 64 kbit/s and can be used for either voice or non-voice operation;

A secondary (B′) channel which operates synchronously at transmission rates up to 8 kbit/s for lower speed non-voice only operation.

A separate (D) channel is also included for the conveyance of signalling information for both B channels.

Only the B and B′ channels are available for connection to a customer's equipments and the D channel is used by the NTE1 itself for signalling (call control) purposes.

The NTE1 is a desk top unit which includes a digital telephone, keypad, display and a single data port. Connection to the data port is via two interface connectors on the unit but only one connector may be used at any one time. One is a 15-pin connector (as specified by ISO 4903) and the other is a 37-pin connector (as specified by ISO 4902).

The NTE1 supports a number of different types of interface and these are:

X.21 but leased line protocols only (15-pin connector);

X.21 bis (37-pin connector);

V.24 start-stop asynchronous operation (connected to 37-pin connector via a 25-pin adapter).

The NTE1 supports the following data rates:

Asynchronous operation up to 9600 bit/s (initially 1200 bit/s);

Synchronous operation at 2400 bit/s, 4800 bit/s, 8000 bit/s, 9600 bit/s, 48 kbit/s or 64 kbit/s.

The NTE1 supports, in conjunction with an appropriate customer terminal, the following types of service:

Circuit switched asynchronous data;

Circuit switched synchronous data;

Facsimile up to 64 kbit/s;

Teletex;

Videotex at 8 kbit/s or 64 kbit/s;

Private Digital Circuits;

Access to PSS;

Slow scan Television;

Telephony services within ISDN and via/to the PSTN.

Network Terminating Equipment No. 3 (NTE3)

This NTE is referred to as a multi-port NTE and provides up to six user ports of which any two may be connected to two digital channels. The NTE3 provides arbitration for the six terminals contending for the two channels. Each port can be one of the following five types:

Full X.21;

X.21 leased line;

X.21 bis;

Analogue 2-wire for connection of an existing telephone or for analogue facsimile equipment;

Modec for interworking with modems (up to 300 bit/s) connected to the PSTN. (A modec combines the functions of a modem and a codec.)

The NTE3 unit is supplied in an enclosure suitable for wall mounting but does not include a telephone handset or keypad. Calls can be initiated either automatically under user control via a full X.21 interface or by using separate remote keypads. Existing telephones (or analogue facsimile equipment) can be connected via an analogue 2-wire port. Figure 6.5 shows a functional block diagram of an NTE.

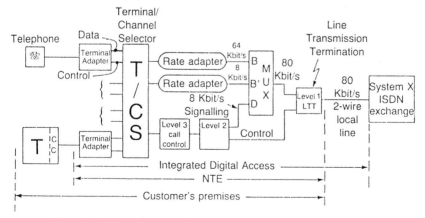

Fig. 6.5. Functional block diagram of an NTE.

Multi-Line IDA

This IDA connection is designed to connect an ISDN System X exchange to a new generation digital PBX. It uses a 2 Mbit/s digital link which carries up to thirty information channels and a common signalling channel. Each information channel operates at 64 kbit/s and can be used for voice or data.

This type of connection is very similar to that provided by the Megastream Service which provides a private 2 Mbit/s connection between two PBXs. In the case of Megastream, a common channel signalling system has been approved by British Telecom and the PBX Industry which is known as DPNSS (Digital Private Network Signalling System). DPNSS is different from the IDA common channel signalling system which is known as DASS (digital access signalling system).
However the Multi-line IDA common channel signalling channel can support both DPNSS and DASS signalling.

A sophisticated and advanced PBX uses all of the Multi-line IDA features to provide integrated voice and data services to its connected extensions. A PBX that provides these functions is referred to as an Integrated Services PBX (ISPBX). A less sophisticated PBX only provides enhanced telephone facilities to its connected extensions; such a PBX is referred to as a Digitally Connected PBX (DCPBX). It is envisaged that many a PBX using Multi-line IDA will start life as a DCPBX and with software enhancements will eventually become an ISPBX.

Multi-line IDA is not limited to PBX connection only but can be used by any customer installation which requires a large number of circuits (e.g. a local area network).

IDA Pilot Service

Major business users are being encouraged to participate in the IDA pilot service to be based on four large System X exchanges, two in London and one each in Birmingham and Manchester. These exchanges will have a total of around 60 access locations. British Telecom plans to increase the number of access locations to around 400 by the end of 1986, and to around 1000 by the end of 1987.

Chapter 7

Multiplexer Networks

INTRODUCTION

This chapter covers the different types of multiplexers used to construct multiplexer networks for data transmission.

The simplest theoretical network that can be configured is a point-to-point multiplexer link using one way (simplex) data transmission. The link operates by combining many data channels at one point, conveying them over one or more circuits/links to a distant point, where the reverse process of separating the channels takes place. At one end of the link a multiplexer combines the data channels and at the other end a demultiplexer separates them.

Multiplexer links normally provide full-duplex channel operation. This requires at each end of the link a multiplexer/demultiplexer (muldex) in a single unit of equipment.

In this book the word "multiplexer" means "multiplexer equipment" and describes a unit which performs both multiplexing and demultiplexing functions.

There are many different types of multiplexer (alternative spelling is multiplexor) at many hierarchal levels. This chapter concentrates on multiplexers which provide channel interfaces for computer/terminals.

TYPES OF MULTIPLEXER

Three main types of multiplexer are used for data transmission:

Frequency Division Multiplexers (FDMs) connected by analogue lines (no modems required);

Time Division Multiplexers (TDMs) normally connected by synchronous links;

Statistical Time Division Multiplexers (STDMs) normally connected by synchronous links.

There does not appear to be an agreed definition for an STDM. In this book STDMs are multiplexers which dynamically allocate the bandwidth of their interconnecting links and support a full-duplex ARQ type protocol (e.g. HDLC, SDLC, DDCMP).

97

MULTIPLEXER CHANNELS

Each multiplexer in a network normally provides one or more of the following channel types for the connection of computer/terminals and voice (speech) equipment:

> Asynchronous data channels (FDMs support only this one data type);

> Non-transparent synchronous data channels supporting a particular type of synchronous protocol (e.g. IBM BSC 3270);

> Transparent synchronous data channels supporting any synchronous protocol;

> A single voice channel provided by FDMs (speech plus duplex operation) connected by analogue lines or by TDMs connected by BT's Kilostream (64 kbit/s) links;

> Many voice channels provided by TDMs connected by BT's Megastream (2 Mbit/s) links.

Asynchronous and synchronous data channels are normally provided with V.24/V.28 (RS-232-C) interfaces operating at transmission rates up to 9600 bit/s or 19,200 bit/s. High speed TDMs can provide V.35 or V.11 (X.21) interfaces for computers requiring higher transmission speeds (e.g. 64 kbit/s).

MAIN CHARACTERISTICS OF DATA MULTIPLEXERS

There is a great variety of multiplexer products and the table opposite is only a general summary. In the table the initials FEC stand for forward error correction (e.g. trellis coding).

FREQUENCY DIVISION MULTIPLEXER

This was the first type of multiplexer to be used for data communications. An FDM divides the frequency bandwidth of a line into a number of individual asynchronous channels where each channel occupies a small part of the total frequency bandwidth (Fig. 7.1). Channels are separated from one another by guard bands (unused bandwidth between channels). Each channel has its own modulator and demodulator; these operate like an asynchronous modem.

For full-duplex operation a 4-wire line is required. In the FDM equipment at each end, all the channel modulators are connected to the transmit pair and all the channel demodulators to the receive pair. The frequency bandwidth (space) taken up by a channel is directly related to the asynchronous transmission rate. The higher the transmission rate, the fewer the number of channels that can be fitted into the frequency bandwidth of a telephone line. For example, at a channel transmission rate of 110 bit/s, the maximum number of channels is eighteen, while at

Type of Multiplexer	Channel Type	Multiplexer Interconnection Characteristics			
		Type of link/line	Frame format	Maximum rate	Error recovery
FDM	Asynchronous or Asynchronous and Voice (S+DX)	Analogue Line	–	–	None
TDM Character-interleaved (OBSOLETE)	V.24/V.28 Asynchronous	Analogue link	Fixed	Up to 19,200 bit/s	None
TDM Integrated into modem	Transparent Synchronous	Analogue Line	Multi-port modem	Up to 19,200 bit/s	None or FEC
TDM Integrated into modem (modem/mux)	Asynchronous and/or Transparent Synchronous	Analogue Line	Statistical	Up to 19,200 bit/s	None or FEC
TDM Bit-interleaved	Asynchronous and/or Transparent Synchronous and/or Voice	Analogue link or Wide-band link or Digital link (Kilostream)	Fixed or Dynamic Bandwidth Allocation	Up to 64 kbit/s	None
TDM Bit-interleaved	Asynchronous and/or Transparent Synchronous and/or Voice	Digital link (Megastream)	Fixed	Up to 2 Mbit/s	None
STDM Character-interleaved (Some STDMs) (use) (integrated) (modems)	Asynchronous and/or Non-Transp. Synchronous and/or Transparent Synchronous	Analogue link or Wide-band link or Digital link (Kilostream)	Statistical	Up to 64 kbit/s	ARQ type protocol (HDLC) (SDLC) (DDCMP)

300 bit/s the maximum number of channels is six. A burst of noise on the line will produce data errors on all channels.

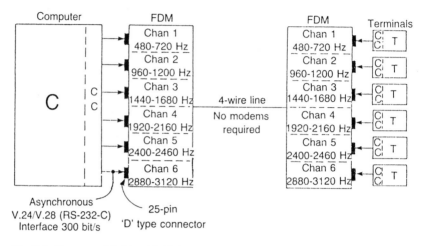

Fig. 7.1. Frequency Division Multiplexer link (6 channels @ 300 bit/s).

As in V.21 300 bit/s modem operation, each FDM channel uses two tones (frequencies) for transmission; one tone represents a binary one and the other a binary zero. In current FDM systems these two tones are both generated in a modulator and switched off and on by the one or zero state of its transmit data interchange circuit. However, when this method of modulation was first introduced one technique was to use a single centre frequency and change (shift) the frequency to a higher frequency for a one and to a lower frequency for a zero. This modulation technique is known as frequency shift keying. There are CCITT 'R' series recommendations for FDM systems which specify for each FDM channel the following parameters:

  Nominal transmission rate in bits per second;

  Centre frequency in Hertz;

  Frequency shift in Hertz (plus and minus)
  dependent on transmission rate;

  Channel spacing between channels in Hertz.

Figure 7.2 shows the bandwidth of a typical telephone line divided into FDM channel allocations for different transmission rates.

A characteristic of FDM systems is the ability to share the line

NOTE: Channel centre frequencies in Hertz are shown in the centre of each box or by an arrow

Maximum number of channels	Data rate bit/s	Frequency shift Hz	Chan spacing Hz
25	75	±30	120
12	150	±60	240
6	300	±120	480
3	600	±240	960
1	1200	±450	1800

| 18 | 110 | ±42.5 | 170 |

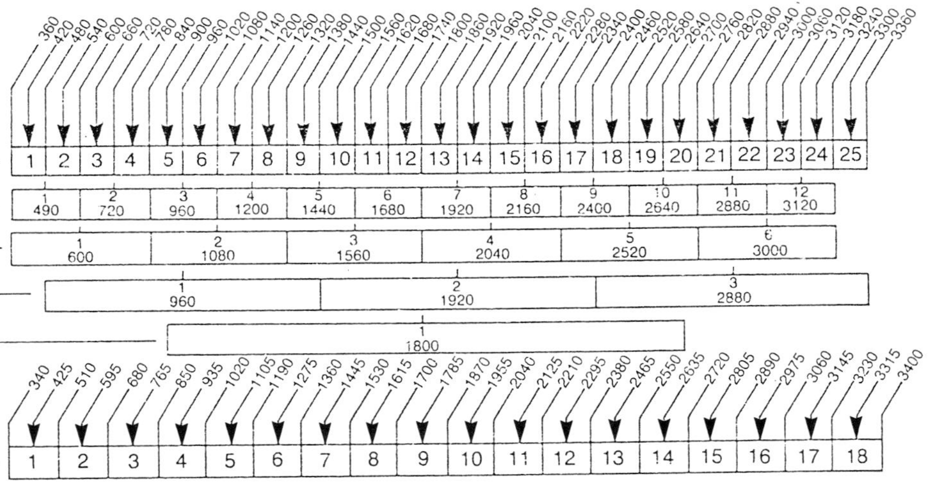

Fig. 7.2. Typical FDM channel allocations.

101

bandwidth between speech and low speed data channels. These systems are known as "speech plus duplex" systems (S+DX) and a few data channels are usually placed above the speech band. One of the present uses of FDM, apart from pure data transmission, is in the field of telemetry. This includes the monitoring and control of remote outstations and the transmission of analogue parameters.

TIME DIVISION MULTIPLEXERS

Time division multiplexers use a type of multiplexing whereby two or more data channels are interleaved in time for transmission over a common (composite) link. A TDM or STDM normally has two basic types of interface:

> A synchronous composite link interface providing communication between multiplexers at each end of a communications link;

> A number of asynchronous and/or synchronous data channel interfaces for the connection of computer/terminals.

Some TDMs have a third type of voice (speech) channel interface.

The synchronous composite interface of a stand-alone multiplexer is normally connected to a synchronous modem (2400–19,200 bit/s), a wide-band modem (48–168 kbit/s) or a digital link (BT's Kilostream or Megastream).

FIXED FRAME TIME DIVISION MULTIPLEXERS

TDMs normally use full-duplex links with frames continuously passing in both directions on the composite link. The first generation of TDMs were bit/character interleaved and used a fixed frame format (Fig. 7.3). A fixed frame TDM constantly scans its data channels for data. Any data found as a result of one or more scans is immediately transmitted in a fixed length frame via the composite link. The composition of a scan can be one bit from each of the data channels (bit interleaved) or one character from each of the data channels (character interleaved). When data rates are low the fixed frame structure is maintained by the TDM which automatically inserts idle bits/characters. When data channels have mixed transmission rates the fastest channels are usually included more than once in a scan.

A TDM removes the start-stop bits from the asynchronous data it receives via its data channels and these are not sent to the composite link. The distant TDM reinstates the start-stop bits when it outputs the asynchronous data to its data channels. The amount of buffering in a fixed frame TDM is minimal and the transmission rate of the composite link is selected to enable all data channels to operate continuously at their selected transmission speed without data loss. This means that the character rate of the composite link is always slightly higher than that of the total aggregate character rate of the data channels.

Character interleaved TDMs are not protected in any way against line noise and a single burst of line noise can affect many asynchronous data channels.

Bit interleaved TDMs also have no protection against line noise. Line noise will produce data errors on transparent synchronous channels but this is usually not a problem because the computer/terminals connected to such channels normally use an ARQ type protocol.

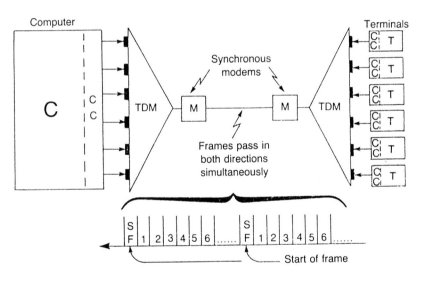

Fig. 7.3. Fixed frame TDM link..

HIGH SPEED FIXED FRAME TIME DIVISION MULTIPLEXERS

The high speed versions of fixed frame bit interleaved TDMs have gained in popularity because they operate with high speed digital links (BT's Kilostream or Megastream service). These high speed TDMs can divide a 2 Mbit/s Megastream link into over fifty individual channels operating at data channel speeds ranging from 50 bit/s to 512 kbit/s. The channels can be asynchronous, transparent synchronous and/or voice channels. Each voice channel normally uses continuously variable slope delta modulation (CVSD) or adaptive differential pulse code modulation (ADPCM) at an effective channel rate of 32 kbit/s. A lower quality voice channel can be provided at an effective channel rate of 16 kbit/s.

A 64 kbit/s Kilostream link can support one 32 kbit/s voice channel and a mix of data channels (e.g. one 19,200 bit/s or two 9600 bit/s).

TIME DIVISION MULTIPLEXERS USING DYNAMIC BANDWIDTH ALLOCATION

TDMs which use dynamic bandwidth allocation normally provide only transparent synchronous channels (no asynchronous channels). A bit-interleaved TDM which uses dynamic bandwidth allocation does not assign a fixed time duration or time slot on the composite link for data channels. Instead, depending on channel activity, it dynamically allocates the composite link bandwidth using a channel priority system. Three types of data channel are normally used; in channel priority order these are "bandsplit", "contention" and "varispeed".

A transparent synchronous channel configured as a "bandsplit" channel is allocated a fixed portion of the composite link bandwidth at a set channel transmission rate.

A transparent synchronous channel configured as a "contention" channel is allocated bandwidth when it is available after raising "request to send". All contention channels usually have equal priority and the first one to raise "request to send" can transmit a data block (frame).

A transparent synchronous channel configured as a "variable speed" (varispeed) channel is allocated a minimum bandwidth to maintain end-to-end communication plus any unused bandwidth released by "bandsplit" or "contention" channels. It operates by varying the mark to space ratio of the transmit clock supplied to the computer/terminal connected to the synchronous channel. When "bandsplit" and "contention" channels are not using their bandwidth, the varispeed channel increases speed and consumes all the unused bandwidth. An STDM can be connected to the "bandsplit" or "varispeed" channel to provide mixed asynchronous and transparent synchronous operation over one link.

Some TDMs only provide a fixed "bandsplit" channel and others provide two or all three types of channel. This type of TDM can be a stand-alone unit or incorporated as a printed circuit board in an STDM.

TIME DIVISION MULTIPLEXERS INTEGRATED INTO SYNCHRONOUS MODEMS

Multi-Port Modem

A multi-port modem is produced by incorporating a simple TDM into a synchronous modem to provide between two and six transparent synchronous channels (ports). The bit interleaved TDM in a multi-port modem does not use a frame structure but simply interleaves the bit streams from each of the transparent synchronous channels. The bit rate of the composite interface (connected internally to the modem) equals the sum of the synchronous channel bit rates (e.g. 9600 bit/s = 4×2400 bit/s). Some synchronous multi-port modems which operate at transmission rates from 9600 bit/s to 19,200 bit/s use forward error correction (FEC) based on trellis coding.

Modem/Multiplexer Unit

A modem/multiplexer unit is a sophisticated TDM incorporated into a synchronous modem. The TDM supports both asynchronous and transparent synchronous channels and statistically multiplexes the channels to/from its composite interface (connected internally to the modem). The synchronous modem used in this combined unit normally operates using forward error correction. The TDM is often referred to as a statistical time division multiplexer but is not classified under that heading in this book because it does not perform an ARQ type protocol.

STATISTICAL TIME DIVISION MULTIPLEXERS

All the early bit/character interleaved TDMs were produced without the use of large scale integration (LSI) circuits (chips). It was the commercial use of LSI (micro-processors) that enabled the first statistical time division multiplexers (STDMs) to be produced. Since then the asynchronous multiplexer market has been dominated by the STDM; the character interleaved fixed frame TDM providing only asynchronous channels is virtually obsolete.

A wide range of STDMs are available with channel capacities from 4/8 channels to many hundreds of channels.

FEATURES PROVIDED BY STATISTICAL TIME DIVISION MULTIPLEXERS

Composite Link

An STDM dynamically allocates the bandwidth of its composite link. A fixed frame format is not used and frames on the composite link can vary both in length and channel data content. Data character positions in a frame are allocated to a data channel only when there are data to send (Fig. 7.4). If only one data channel is active then all the data character positions in a frame can be allocated to that channel. When all the data channels are active then a priority system ensures that no channel hogs all the data character positions in the frames.

More channels can be attached to an STDM than to a fixed frame TDM because time is not wasted in sending idle characters.

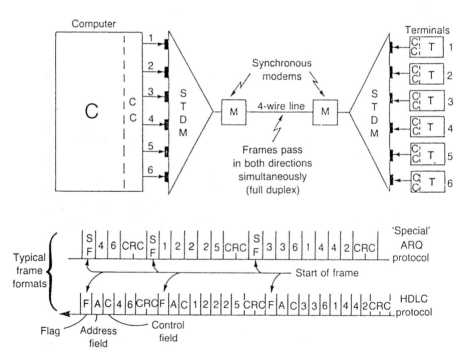

Fig. 7.4. Statistical Time Division Multiplexer link.

One of the advantages of STDMs is that they use an ARQ (automatic request for retransmission) type protocol on the composite link; any block of data corrupted due to line noise will be retransmitted.

Normally a full-duplex protocol such as HDLC, SDLC, DDCMP or some variant is used. Operation over multiple satellite links will involve the use of extended send/receive sequence counts (see Chapter 15).

If line quality is poor an STDM spends vast amounts of time retransmitting data blocks and its channel throughput suffers. Fortunately an STDM keeps running totals on the number of blocks sent/received and the number of line errors so that a poor quality line can be identified.

STDMs provide remote connection for asynchronous terminals which do not use an ARQ type protocol. The ARQ protocol on the composite link ensures that a terminal's data is transferred without error. This type of connection is frequently used to connect groups of asynchronous terminals in one or more remote locations to a central computer system.

The error free asynchronous modem also provides this ARQ function for a single asynchronous terminal at a remote location.

Multiple Composite Links

A high proportion of STDM links are point-to-point links. With this type of link an STDM at one end communicates via a synchronous link to an STDM at the other end. By using two composite links at one location (e.g. location B) it is possible to connect terminals at location B and location C to a computer system at location A. The composite link connecting A to B carries channels for B and C while the composite link between B and C carries only channels for C (Fig. 7.5).

Two locations can be connected together by two composite links and the traffic load between these sites can be shared by the two links. If one link should fail then the total traffic load is handled by the remaining composite link.

The interconnection possibilities are powerful and in a large network there can be well over 50 interconnected STDM locations.

Data Buffers

To average out the traffic peaks, an STDM uses large data buffers to buffer traffic to/from its data channels.

The amount of traffic that can be generated by a group of terminals attached to an STDM is well below the continuous transmission rate of each terminal for the following reasons.

With character mode terminals the character rate when sending messages is reduced to typing speed. An STDM can provide local

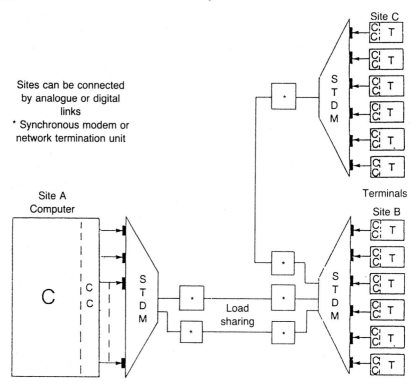

Fig. 7.5. Multiple composite links.

character echo for full-duplex character mode terminals; this saves bandwidth on the composite link.

An interactive block mode terminal does not usually transmit while waiting for a message, while receiving a message and during message preparation. However there will be times when all block mode terminals transmit simultaneously.

Data Flow Control

STDM Flow Control

An STDM uses data flow control to stop incoming data from a computer/terminal when its data buffer is in danger of overflowing. There are two methods by which an STDM can signal to a computer/terminal to stop sending.

The first method is to send to the computer/terminal a character which is interpreted as "stop sending". When buffer space becomes available the STDM sends a character to the computer/terminal which is interpreted as "continue sending". Characters used for this purpose are normally IA5 data control characters DC1, DC2 or DC3. This method is known as "in band" flow control.

The second method of flow control is for the STDM to use an interchange circuit in the V.24/V.28 (RS-232-C) channel interface. The signal normally used is interchange circuit 106 "ready for sending/clear to send" which appears on pin 5 of the 25-way connector. To signal "stop sending" the STDM changes RFS/CTS to the off ($-V$) state and to signal "continue sending" the STDM changes RFS/CTS to the on ($+V$) state. This method is known as "out of band" flow control.

An STDM normally signals "stop sending" when its buffer is about 65% full and signals "continue sending" when its buffer is about 40% full. Block mode computer/terminals do not respond immediately to "stop sending" commands so 35% of the buffer is reserved to allow current transmissions to finish.

An STDM can use a mixture of in-band and out-of-band flow control at the two channel ends of a link.

Many computers/terminals do not respond to flow control commands. To minimise the chance of buffer overflow, larger buffers are normally installed in the STDMs.

Computer/Terminal Flow Control

Computer/terminal flow control is used to prevent data output from an STDM channel overflowing the buffers of a computer/terminal. STDMs will respond to these flow control commands. Computer/terminal flow control is the same as STDM flow control except that the "in band" and "out of band" commands are in the opposite direction. (i.e. computer/terminal to STDM). For "out of band" flow control an interchange circuit with a signal direction from computer/terminal to STDM is required. The one normally used is interchange circuit 108/2 "data terminal ready" (pin 20).

Number of Asynchronous Channels

Manufacturers of STDMs quote figures for the number of asynchronous data channels that can be provided at a given channel rate (bit/s). As a rule of thumb, the total aggregate asynchronous channel rate in bits per second can be four times the transmission rate of the synchronous composite link. This rule applies to a reasonable number of channels (say eight or more) operating at low transmission rates. When there are only a few channels operating at high transmission rates the figure of four should be reduced to two. For the most efficient operation no single channel should operate at the same transmission rate as the composite link. Obviously the larger the number of asynchronous channels, the lower the probability of them all being active at the same time. The following is a typical calculation:

Composite transmission rate 9600 bit/s

Total aggregate channel rate is
4×9600 bit/s $= 38,400$ bit/s.

This aggregate channel rate should support the following number of asynchronous channels:

Eight asynchronous channels at 4800 bit/s

Sixteen asynchronous channels at 2400 bit/s

Thirty-two asynchronous channels at 1200 bit/s.

User Switching

User switching is a facility offered by STDM networks. It provides a user with the ability to select (via his/her asynchronous terminal connected to the network) a connection to a destination channel, one of a group of channels, or a "gateway" anywhere on the network. The selection is performed by a "dialogue" between the user's terminal and the STDM to which it is attached. User switching provides a user with access to any one of a number of computer systems (services) connected to the network or to services outside the network.

Auto-Answer and Password Checking

A terminal user need not be permanently connected to an STDM but can dial-in using an acoustic coupler or a V.21/V.22 modem. STDMs have the ability to auto-answer dial-in calls and some can request and check a password entered from the keyboard by the remote user. This procedure can prevent illegal access to an STDM network.

Dial-in access to an STDM network can be coupled with user switching to allow a dial-in remote user access to a wide range of network services. The computer systems which use these network services normally have their own password protection in addition to that provided by the network.

Automatic Bit Rate Detection

The asynchronous transmission rate in bit/s of an "asynchronous device" is usually set up within the device by software, switch settings or hardware straps. In a point to point multiplexer link, the term "asynchronous device" can be applied to the asynchronous computer/terminal at each end of the link, and also to the asynchronous channels of the two multiplexers at each end. STDM channels normally operate using the same asynchronous bit rate at each end of a link but can operate with different bit rates if required. However, for correct operation an STDM channel and its locally connected asynchronous computer/terminal must be set up to operate at the same bit rate.

On some time sharing services the asynchronous ports of the computer system are set up for automatic bit rate (ABR) detection. A port checks the first received character and determines from this the bit rate being used by the attached terminal. This function is normally used on a dial-in port and allows terminals with different bit rates to be connected (one at a time) to the same port.

When dial-in is not direct to the computer system but is via an STDM network then the STDM channels used in the connection are set up to perform ABR detection. A dial-in user may have to send two bit rate detection characters: one to satisfy the answering STDM channel (which will pass the bit rate to the far end channel) and the other to satisfy the computer system port after the STDM link has been established. Usually one bit rate character will satisfy both the STDM channels and the computer system port.

Polling Multiplexers

Polling STDMs are used on synchronous 4-wire multipoint links (see Chapter 5). They use a synchronous poll/select protocol on the multipoint link and provide asynchronous channels for computer/terminals enabling them to communicate via the link. Two models of polling STDM are normally provided. One model (poll/select master) is used at the multipoint centre and has a number of asynchronous channels, one for each remote asynchronous terminal connected to the multipoint link. The other model (poll/select slave) has only one or two asynchronous channels and is used in each remote location to connect one or two asynchronous terminals to the multipoint link. The polling STDM at the multipoint centre is usually connected to the asynchronous ports of a computer system but could be connected to terminals, to provide central terminal to remote terminal operation, if required. Polling STDMs are a specialised product and many STDMs do not provide this function.

Other Features

The following is a list of other important STDM features:

Echoplex (character echo);

Supervisory channel;

Network Management capability;

Diagnostics and inbuilt indicators;

Down-line loading;

Operation over satellite links;

The transport of synchronous protocols;

The provision of "gateway" functions allowing terminals on an STDM network connection to X.25 Packet Switched Data Networks and Host Computers (e.g. IBM);

Support of computer manufacturer's special requirements, for example:

Hewlett Packard's ENQ/ACK protocol;

Tandem's T-pause "out of band" flow control;

Wang's special "in band" flow control.

Chapter 8

Packet Switched Data Networks

INTRODUCTION

A Packet Switched Data Network (PSDN) is a public or private data network which conforms to CCITT Recommendation X.25.

X.25 defines "an interface between data terminal equipment (DTE) and data circuit-terminating equipment (DCE) for terminals operating in the packet mode on public data networks". Though not specifically mentioned in the title the interface is synchronous.

The word "terminals" means any DTE which can perform X.25; for example, a main-frame computer system, a mini-computer system, a micro-computer system, or micro-processor based system. For ease of explanation, the word "computer" will be used for an X.25 DTE unless there is a need to mention a specific type of X.25 DTE.

An asynchronous start-stop mode terminal interfaces to a PSDN via a PAD (Packet Assembler/Disassembler) which conforms to CCITT Recommendations X.3, X.28 and X.29 (Triple-X). One PAD normally provides interface for 8, 16 or 24 asynchronous terminals.

A Packet Switched Data Network consists of switching nodes (packet switching exchanges [PSEs]) located in different geographical locations and connected together by high-speed transmission links (Fig. 8.1). The network is designed to overcome link failures between PSEs by alternative routing (rerouting). The network is normally configured, controlled and run from a Network Management System located at one of the PSE sites.

A PSDN provides the means of communicating between computers, between computers and terminals, and between terminals.

A PACKET

A packet is a quantity of data, usually 128 octets (an octet is 8 bits), which is routed through a packet switched network to its destination using an address contained in the packet. For example, if computer A has a large quantity of data to send to another computer on the network, computer B, then computer A sends the data as a number of separate

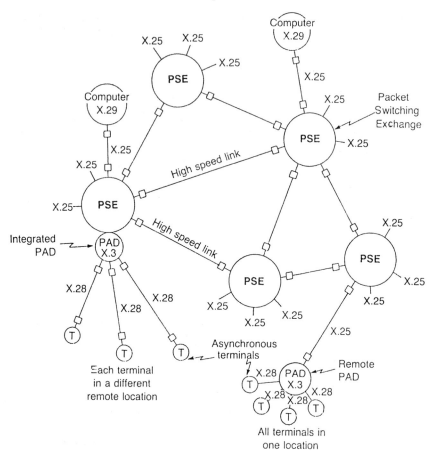

Fig. 8.1. Packet Switched Data Network (PSDN).

packets and each packet is individually routed to computer B. Computer A can also send data to computer C at the same time. In this case computer A transmits, through its single link to the network, interleaved packets for computer B and for computer C. These are individually routed to their destinations. Therefore, a packet switched network offers each connected computer/PAD a form of packet multiplexing.

Before packets can be transmitted through a PSDN network, a connection has to be established between the source computer/PAD and the destination computer/PAD. There are two types of connection: a switched virtual circuit (SVC) and a permanent virtual circuit (PVC).

SWITCHED VIRTUAL CIRCUIT

A switched virtual circuit (SVC) can be compared in operation to the Public Switched Telephone Network (PSTN). To make a connection, the network number (network user address — NUA) of the computer/PAD must be known.

CCITT X.121 recommendation specifies an international numbering plan for public data networks.

A Network User Address (NUA) consists of twelve decimal digits plus two optional digits.

Digits		Digits	
1–4	DNIC	1–3	Country
		4	Network
4–12	National Number	4	Network
		5–7	Local Number Area
		8–12	Local Number
13, 14	Subaddress (one or two optional digits)		

The first four digits are known as the "data network identification code" (DNIC); of these the first three are used to identify a country, and the fourth a network within the country. Digits four to twelve are known as the "national number". Each connection to a packet switched network has an individual national number.

With SVC type connections a computer/PAD initiates the connection of a virtual circuit by sending a "call request" packet containing an NUA. After the connection has been confirmed and data has been transmitted/received, then the virtual circuit connection is cleared (disconnected) by sending a "clear request" packet. A single physical X.25 communications link between a computer and a packet switched data network can support many simultaneous SVCs.

PERMANENT VIRTUAL CIRCUIT

A permanent virtual circuit (PVC) can be compared to a leased circuit in that no call set-up or clear down is required. The interchange of data packets can take place at any time on a PVC. PVCs are assigned by the PSDN network management system.

X.25 RECOMMENDATION

The X.25 Recommendation specifies a packet mode interface between a computer and a packet switched data network.

The International Standards Organisation (ISO) has recommended a Basic Model for Open Systems Interconnection (OSI). This ISO model defines seven layers or levels and X.25 conforms to the first three layers.

Open Systems Interconnection		X.25 Description
Layer No.	Description	
3	Network	Packet level
2	Data Link	High-level data link control (HDLC)
1	Physical	X.21 preferred X.21 bis optional

Layer One

The physical interface is between a computer and the communications link that connects the computer to the network. If the link is a digital link, then the physical interface is specified by X.21. However, if the link is an analogue link (using modems), then the physical interface is specified by X.21 bis.

X.21 Recommendation

"General purpose interface between data terminal equipment (DTE) and data circuit-terminating equipment (DCE) for synchronous operation on public data networks"

X.21 bis Recommendation

"Use on public data networks for data terminal equipments (DTEs) which are designed for interfacing to synchronous Series V Recommendations modems"

Layer Two

A subset of HDLC is used for the Data Link level and provides the link with an automatic retransmission capability to overcome line errors.

HDLC is described in Chapter 15 and its frame format is shown in Fig. 8.2.

A choice of two Link Access Procedures are provided (LAPB is preferred).

Link Access Procedure (LAP), based on
HDLC Asynchronous Response Mode (ARM) Symmetrical Operation

Link Access Procedure Balanced (LAPB), based on
HDLC Asynchronous Balanced Mode (ABM)

Layer Three

The "network" level is implemented using 14 different packet types. The general packet format is shown in Fig. 8.2. All the packet types are listed in the following table and a packet direction from A to B is assumed.

Computer A -- Link --(N e t w o r k)-- Link -- Computer B
     DTE   DCE   DCE   DTE

Call Request	Incoming Call
Call Accepted	Call Connected
Clear Request	Clear Indication
DTE Clear Confirmation	DCE Clear Confirmation
DTE Data	DCE Data
DTE Interrupt	DCE Interrupt
DTE Interrupt Confirmation	DCE Interrupt Confirmation
DTE Receive Ready	DCE Receive Ready
DTE Receive Not Ready	DCE Receive Not Ready
DTE Reject	
Reset Request	Reset Indication
DTE Reset Confirmation	DCE Reset Confirmation
Restart Request	Restart Indication
DTE Restart Confirmation	DCE Restart Confirmation

The first four packet types on the list are used for SVC call set-up and clearing. The next three are for data interchange and interrupt. The next five provide flow control and reset functions and the final two are for restart.

A packet can have a different interpretation depending upon whether it is entering or leaving a packet switched data network. For example, suppose that computer A sends a "call request" packet to

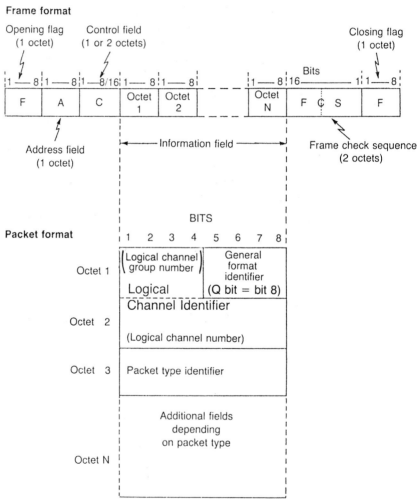

Note: Octets in a packet are transmitted low order bit first (bit 1). The FCS is transmitted high order bit first (bit 16).

Fig. 8.2. General packet format.

computer B, then computer B treats it as an "incoming call" packet. If computer B accepts the call, then it sends to computer A a "call accepted" packet which is interpreted by computer A as a "call connected" packet.

VIRTUAL CIRCUIT ASSIGNMENT

Virtual circuits are described in the general packet format (Fig. 8.2) as "logical channels" and have a logical channel identifier of 12 bits. This identifier is normally split into a logical channel group number of 4 bits and a logical channel number of 8 bits. A group can have up to 256 logical channels (except for group 0 which can have only 255). There can be up to 16 groups and therefore the theoretical maximum number of virtual circuits for any one X.25 connection to a PSDN is 4095 ($16 \times 256 - 1$).

In the UK the public packet switched data network is called Packet SwitchStream (PSS). The PSS offers four types of logical channels.

Permanent Virtual Circuit (PVC)
PSS uses its own term and calls this a Permanent Data Call.

Switched Virtual Circuit (SVC)
PSS calls this a Data Call. There are three types; all provide full-duplex operation but differ in the way calls can be set up:

Incoming only SVC

Both way SVC

Outgoing only SVC.

The UK PSS provides up to eight logical channel groups for each physical X.25 connection.

Group	Type	
0	PVC	
1	PVC	
2	SVC	Incoming calls only
3	SVC	Incoming calls only
4	SVC	Both way calls
5	SVC	Both way calls
6	SVC	Outgoing calls only
7	SVC	Outgoing calls only

For PSS the theoretical maximum number of virtual circuits per physical X.25 network connection (PSS port) is 2047 ($8 \times 256 - 1$).

As stated earlier, PVCs are permanently assigned and a computer knows that a packet addressed to PSS group 0 channel 1 always goes, for example, to computer X.

SVCs are not permanently assigned but are used when calls are made and become available for re-use when calls are cleared. All packet types except "restart request" packets contain a logical channel identifier. In the case of SVCs the "call request" packet is the only packet type which contains X.121 addresses.

On an outgoing SVC call, a computer finds its highest free logical channel in a group and sends a "call request" packet containing this group/channel number, the destination X.121 address and optionally its own X.121 address.

On an incoming call, the packet switching exchange (PSE) finds the lowest free channel number in a group on the destination computer port and inserts that logical group/channel number into the "incoming call" (call request) packet.

After an SVC connection has been made, the computers address their packets using their logical group/channel numbers and the PSEs in the network perform the packet routing and conversion of the logical group/channel numbers.

When an SVC connection is cleared, then the logical group/channel numbers assigned at both ends of the connection are freed and become available for re-use.

Only the PSEs in the network know the association between the PSE node/port assigned to a DTE, X.121 addresses and logical group/channel numbers.

With a computer assigning the highest free channel number to each outgoing call and its PSE assigning the lowest free channel number to each incoming call, a clash of assignments is avoided. This clash can also be avoided by using two logical groups: one for incoming calls only and one for outgoing calls only.

Before connecting to a PSDN, a user has to state how many PVCs and SVCs are required per physical X.25 network connection point (port). In the case of public PSDNs, each PVC and SVC normally incurs an annual rental.

PAD CONNECTION

Asynchronous terminals are connected to a packet switched data network via integrated or remote packet assembler/disassemblers (PADs).

An integrated PAD is usually incorporated with its PSE in a PSE cabinet. In this case each asynchronous terminal located at a remote site is connected via a separate communications link (X.28) to its integrated PAD. Alternatively, a remote PAD (small free-standing unit) can be located at a remote site connected via a single communications link (X.25) to its PSE. A remote PAD will normally connect up to 8 or 16 asynchronous terminals at a remote site to a PSE.

An integrated PAD can be shared by a number of terminals at different remote locations, but a remote PAD is usually dedicated to terminals at one location.

There is another aspect regarding the location of PADs and that concerns line noise on the communications link and communications protocols.

A remote PAD communicates with its PSE using X.25 over the connecting link. X.25 uses a subset of HDLC as its data link protocol and therefore data which is corrupted due to line noise is automatically retransmitted.

X.28 procedures are used by an asynchronous terminal to talk to an integrated PAD and these procedures do not contain any retransmission on error capability. Therefore the link between an asynchronous terminal and an integrated PAD is not protected against data errors due to line noise.

PAD Operation

Operation of a PAD is specified in the following CCITT Triple-X Recommendations:

X.3 Recommendation

"Packet assembly/disassembly facility (PAD) in a public data network"

X.28 Recommendation

"DTE/DCE interface for a start-stop mode data terminal equipment accessing the packet assembly/disassembly facility (PAD) on a public data network situated in the same country"

X.29 Recommendation

"Procedures for exchange of control information and user data between a packet mode DTE and a packet assembly/disassembly facility (PAD)".

PAD Functions

The X.3 recommendation lists the basic functions of a PAD:

Assembly of characters (received from an asynchronous terminal) into packets;

Disassembly of the user data field in packets and output to an asynchronous terminal;

Handling of virtual call set-up and clearing, resetting and interrupt procedures;

Generation of service signals;

The provision of a mechanism for forwarding packets when the proper conditions exists; such as when a packet is full, a data forwarding character is received, or an idle timer expires due to operator inactivity;

Transmission of data characters including start, stop and parity bits as required by the connected asynchronous terminal;

Detection of a "break" signal from an asynchronous terminal;

Editing of PAD command sequences.

X.3 PAD Parameters

A PAD has the ability to store parameters and these are normally held in non-volatile memory in the PAD. These parameters can be set up either via an asynchronous terminal connected to the PAD or by any one of the computers connected to the packet switched network which obeys X.29. These parameters are referred to in the CCITT X.29 Recommendation as control information. Therefore, there is a need to qualify data which passes between a computer and a PAD as either control information (PAD messages) or genuine data from/to an asynchronous terminal. This is accomplished by a single qualifier bit (the Q bit) contained in every packet; when the Q bit is a one the packet contains a PAD message and when it is a zero the packet contains genuine data.

In a control information packet a 4-bit code in the first octet of the PAD message field indicates the type of message.

Code	Pad Message	Sent by
0001	Invitation to Clear	Computer
0010	Set Parameters	Computer
0011	Indication of Break	Computer or PAD

0100	Read Parameters	Computer
0101	Error	PAD
0110	Set and Read Parameters	Computer

Any number of parameters can be included in a PAD message field subject to the maximum packet size. Each PAD parameter is referenced by a number from one upwards and this number precedes its parameter values.

Parameter	Description
1	PAD recall using a character
2	Echo
3	Selection of Data Forwarding Characters
4	Selection of idle timer delay
5	Ancillary device control
6	Suppression of PAD service signals
7	Selection of operation of PAD on receipt of break
8	Discard output
9	Padding after carriage return
10	Line folding (maximum display line length)
11	Binary speed of start-stop mode DTE (terminal)
12	Flow control of PAD
13	Line feed insertion after carriage return
14	Padding after line feed
15	Editing
16	Character delete
17	Line delete
18	Line display
19	Editing PAD service signals
20	Echo mask
21	Parity treatment
22	Page wait

PAD Profiles

The UK PSS provides the user of a start-stop mode terminal with the means of selecting a set of PAD parameters with predefined values. The user sends to the PSS integrated PAD a profile selection command which includes a profile identifier. This identifies one of a number of standard profiles held in the PAD.

The profile identifier plus PAD parameter 11 (terminal speed) are included in the "call user data field" of "call request" packets sent by PSS PADs. Using this field the called computer/PAD derives information concerning the calling start-stop mode terminal.

Reverse PAD

A reverse PAD, sometimes called a host PAD, is used to connect asynchronous hosts (computers) to an X.25 network. Each asynchronous connection from a reverse PAD to its asynchronous host (computer) supports only one virtual channel. Eight virtual channels require eight asynchronous connections (ports) on the PAD.

GATEWAYS TO STATISTICAL MULTIPLEXER NETWORKS

The majority of manufacturers of statistical multiplexer equipments provide a "gateway" between their equipment and an X.25 network. The "gateway" is normally connected to the X.25 network by an X.25 link and operates like a remote PAD to connect asynchronous terminals on the multiplexer network to the X.25 network.

IBM 3270 PROTOCOL CONVERSION

Protocol converters exist which provide IBM 3270 BSC or SNA operation between an IBM Host and an IBM 3270 Clustered Display System (or equivalent) via an X.25 network. For correct operation two protocol converter models are required; a host end unit for connection between an IBM Host and an X.25 network and a terminal end unit for connection between an IBM clustered display system and an X.25 network.

THE UK PUBLIC PACKET SWITCHED DATA SERVICE (PSS)

PSS (Packet Switchstream) is a UK data communications service offered by British Telecom. It is a national, public, packet switched data service and provides full-duplex operation at transmission rates from 110 bit/s to 48 kbit/s.

British Telecom identifies two types of "terminal" for connection to the PSS Network, a "packet terminal" known as a DTE-P and a "character terminal" known as a DTE-C.

The PSS provides a communication link between "terminals" operating at different speeds. For example, a packet terminal (DTE-P) operating synchronously at 2400–48,000 bit/s can communicate with an asynchronous character terminal (DTE-C) operating at 110–1200 bit/s.

Packet Terminal

A packet terminal is an intelligent device (e.g. micro-computer, mini-computer, computer or external PAD) which communicates synchro-nously at 2400 bit/s, 4800 bit/s, 9600 bit/s or 48 kbit/s with the PSS using the PSS three level protocol (X.25). This synchronous connection to the PSS can be provided only by British Telecom and is known as a "Data-line". A Dataline rental includes the charges for the packet terminal's modem, the leased line to the PSS exchange, and for the modem plus dedicated port in the PSS exchange. The important difference between Datalines and normal leased line connections is that the Dataline charges are completely independent of the distance between a packet terminal and the nearest PSS exchange.

Character Terminal

A character terminal is a terminal such as a teletype compatible VDU or a teletypewriter which communicates asynchronously at 110 bit/s, 300 bit/s, 75/1200 bit/s or 1200 bit/s with PSS using the PSS PAD (X.28) procedures. A character terminal which operates at 75/1200 bit/s, sends at 75 bit/s and receives at 1200 bit/s.

Character terminals connect to an integrated PSS Packet Assembler/ Disassembler located within each PSS exchange.

The asynchronous full-duplex connection to a PSS PAD can be a dial-up connection at 110 bit/s, 300 bit/s, 75/1200 bit/s or 1200 bit/s; or a Dataline (leased line) connection at 300 bit/s or 1200 bit/s. In the case of dial-up connection, a character terminal's modem is either a V.21 mod-em, a V.23 modem or a V.22 modem.

A dial-up connection has an additional requirement which is the allocation by British Telecom of a Network User Identity (NUI) for which a rental is charged.

PSS Tariff Structure

The PSS tariff structure is made up of three parts.

Access

The access tariffs include all charges required to connect to the PSS exchange (i.e. Dataline charges, modem charges, PSTN con-nection charges, NUI charges etc).

Usage

The usage tariffs are based on the call duration (i.e. x pence per hour) and the quantity of data (packets) carried (x pence per kilosegment). A segment is equal to 0–64 octets (an octet is 8 bits) and is equivalent to half a packet. (Standard Rate 8.00 am – 6.00 pm, Monday to Friday; Cheap Rate at all other times).

Facilities

The facilities tariffs include charges for:

> Close User Group (CUG)
> Transfer Charge Acceptance
> Minicall Acceptance
> Permanent Datacall (PDC)
> Logical Channels
> Multiline
> Call Redirection
> Dataline to Alternative PSS Exchange.

PSS Network Configuration

When the service first started PSS Exchanges were located in the following places:

> Birmingham
> Bristol
> Cambridge
> Edinburgh
> Glasgow
> Leeds
> Liverpool
> London
> Manchester
> Newcastle
> Reading
> Slough.

Since then the network has expanded and is still being expanded. By 1988 it is estimated that the number of PSS exchanges will be 80 or more.

Connection of a Character Terminal (DTE-C)

There are six possible ways to connect a character terminal to a PSS integrated PAD (Fig. 8.3):

A Dataline 300 (V.21) leased line connection (300 bit/s);

A Dataline 1200 (V.23) leased line connection (1200 bit/s);

An acoustic coupler (V.21) dial-up connection (300 bit/s);

A V.21 modem dial-up connection (300 bit/s);

A V.23 modem dial-up connection (75/1200 bit/s);

A V.22 modem dial-up connection (1200 bit/s).

A character terminal is normally a standalone VDU (character mode device) plus a document printer if required. Printing is initiated by the terminal operator pressing the print key to print the screen contents on the printer.

Dataline costs are independent of distance between the terminal operator's office and the nearest PAD.

The PSTN dial-up connections have a higher usage cost per hour than Dataline connections and the PSTN connection charges depend upon the distance between the terminal operator's office and the PAD and also the time of day.

The following calls are permissible via a PSS integrated PAD:

Dataline DTE-C calling a Dataline DTE-C or a Dataline DTE-P;

PSTN DTE-C calling a Dataline DTE-C or a Dataline DTE-P;

Dataline DTE-P calling a Dataline DTE-C.

For a Dataline connected DTE-C the operator identifies the required network connection by typing in its "network user address" (NUA). This is 9–11 numeric characters for a UK NUA, because the three-digit country code is not required. For an international call, the NUA is prefixed by a single 9 digit, so a maximum of 15 numeric characters could be required.

For a dial-up connection, the terminal operator first manually dials the PAD and awaits confirmation of a PSTN connection. When connected to the PAD, the operator types in the 12 alpha-numeric characters of his/her "network user identity" (NUI) and proceeds as for a Dataline connection.

The PAD provides character echo operation which enables the terminal operator to check visually the data sent to the PAD.

The most serious disadvantage of the PSS integrated PAD is the lack of any line protocol to ensure error-free operation on data sent from the PAD to a VDU.

A remote PAD provides error-free operation but is connected to PSS as a "packet terminal" (DTE-P).

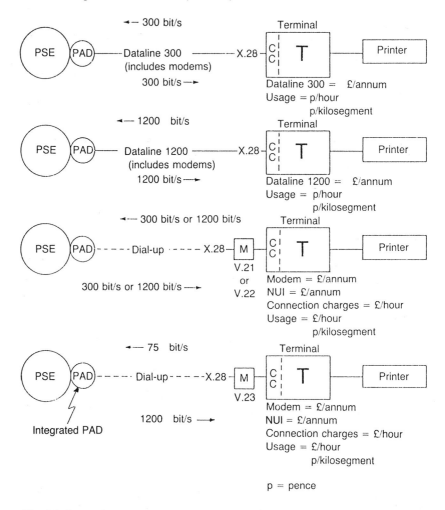

Fig. 8.3. Connection of an asynchronous DTE-C to PSS.

Connection of a Packet Terminal (DTE-P)

Figure 8.4 shows three examples of connecting a "packet terminal" to the PSS. A VDU has been chosen as the device to be connected (directly or indirectly) so that a comparison can be made with Fig. 8.3.

The first configuration shows a single VDU programmed to handle the X.25 protocol. VDUs are available which can perform this function.

The second configuration shows a number of asynchronous VDUs connected to a remote PAD where the PAD performs the X.25 protocol. A remote PAD can normally connect up to 8 or 16 asynchronous VDU terminals.

The third configuration shows a disk-based computer system with communications interfaces for the connection of local and/or remote stand-alone or clustered VDU systems. The alternative exchange connection shown on the configuration provides for an alternative path into the PSS network should the original dataline connection or PSS exchange fail.

Where a large number of VDUs are connected to the PSS (indirectly) via a mini-computer, then the cost of an alternative exchange connection to provide a form of standby operation could be justified.

BRITISH TELECOM SERVICES THAT CONNECT TO PSS

Multistream

British Telecom has introduced another stream service for its PSS. This service is called MultiStream and offers a range of new PSS access services called EPAD and VPAD provided by packet multiplexers deployed in local telephone exchanges.

Multistream EPAD is an asynchronous access service to PSS which provides error protection on the data path by using EPAD software in either the modem or intelligent terminal at a customer's site.

Multistream VPAD is a dial-up videotex access service designed to meet the needs of users of private videotex (Viewdata) systems. The service provides access from videotex terminals with call set-up controlled by on-screen menus.

Interstream

Interstream is a family of three gateways currently under development by British Telecom for interconnection with Packet Switch Stream (PSS).

Interstream One

Interstream One provides a link between the Telex network and the PSS network.

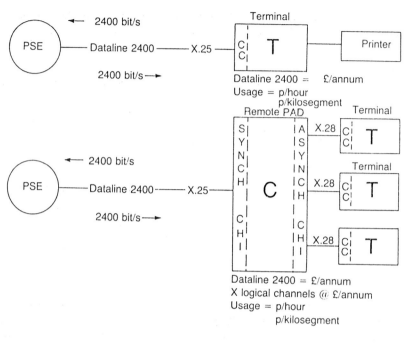

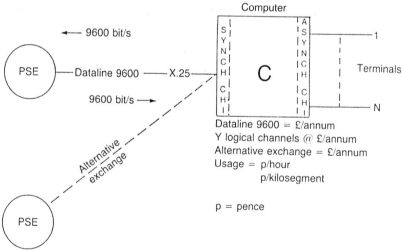

Fig. 8.4. Connection of a synchronous DTE-P to PSS.

A Telex subscriber can set up a call and once established transfer information with a PSS subscriber and vice-versa.

Interstream Two

Interstream Two provides a link between the Public Switched Telephone Network (PSTN) and PSS. Calls can be set up in either direction between the PSTN and PSS. Teletex users on the PSTN and PSS are able to use Interstream Two to intercommunicate.

Interstream Three

Interstream Three provides Teletex terminals connected to the PSTN or to the PSS with interworking links to the Telex service. It operates on a store and forward principle holding each access circuit for only as long as is needed to send or receive a message.

Prestel Gateway

Prestel Gateway is a gateway between Prestel and PSS. It allows a user with a conventional Prestel (Viewdata) terminal to communicate (via Prestel and its PSS gateway) with an X.25 connected "external" computer. It provides a Prestel user with the ability to retrieve information from or pass information to any "external" computer connected to PSS.

Chapter 9

Local Area Networks — Introduction

INTRODUCTION

The last few years have seen the introduction of a wide variety of products for the construction of Local Area Networks (LANs).

This chapter is a general introduction to the different types of LAN and the standards that apply.

TERMINOLOGY

One of the main difficulties in describing LAN systems is the wide variety of terms used by authors of LAN standards and by product manufacturers.

In describing LANs, the following terms are used.

Broadband Transmission

Broadband transmission uses radio frequency modems to convey digital information over the transmission medium. By operating modems at different frequencies (frequency division multiplexing) a single transmission medium can support a number of simultaneous information channels without disruption.

Baseband Transmission

Baseband transmission uses direct encoding to convey digital information over the transmission medium (radio frequency modems are not used). At any time only one information signal can be present on the transmission medium without disruption.

Transmission Medium

This is the physical medium (e.g. cable) used to convey data over a LAN. It includes any active hardware (e.g. amplifiers) required to regenerate signals on the medium and/or passive hardware (e.g. tap) required to provide physical access to the medium.

Medium Attachment Unit (MAU)

This is the active hardware (e.g. transceiver, R.F. modem) required to send/receive data signals to/from the medium. (Active hardware is hardware [equipment] that requires external power for its operation; passive hardware does not require any power for its operation.)

LAN Controller

A LAN Controller is a product offered by manufacturers which is generally micro-processor based and which is programmed to enable devices (computer/terminals) to communicate via the LAN. A Controller may contain the medium attachment unit (RF modem).

User Device

Usually abbreviated to device, this is a general term for a main-frame computer system, mini-computer system, micro-computer system, or terminal connected as a user to a LAN.

Station

A Station (Node) is equipment that has a single point of physical attachment to a LAN. It normally consists of a free standing LAN Controller and/or printed circuit boards (PCBs) which plug into attached devices to allow connection to a LAN.

LAN APPLICATIONS

A LAN is a communications network that covers a limited geographical area and provides an interconnection mechanism for a wide range of applications:

Communication between computers;

Communication between terminals;

Communication between office automation equipment;

Terminal to computer (host) access;

Resource sharing enabling several devices (e.g. personal computers, office automation equipment etc.) to share a single hard disk (file server) and/or a hard copy printer (print server);

Sharing of common facilities (data, voice, video, communication services etc.) between various computer/terminal/office applications.

LAN CHARACTERISTICS

There are many different LAN products but they usually have the following common characteristics.

A LAN normally supports a high serial data transmission rate on the medium with low error rates. The actual transmission rate depends on the product being used but is generally between 100 kbit/s and 10 Mbit/s.

A LAN uses either broadband transmission or baseband transmission and one or a combination of the following topologies:

Bus;
Ring;
Star;
Tree.

The LAN transmission medium provides a high degree of interconnection between stations. The main part of the medium is normally cable (except for LANs using a star topology) but there could be other components involved (e.g. amplifiers or regenerative electronic circuitry). The cable used for the medium can be one of a number of types:

Semi-rigid coaxial cable;
Flexible coaxial cable;
Twisted pair cable;
Fibre-optic cable;
Multi-wire ribbon/round cable.

The total length of a LAN can be anything from a few metres to several kilometres.

Many products include "servers" which provide common services for devices attached to the LAN. These services are generally implemented on micro-processor or mini-computer systems (with attached peripherals) which are connected to the LAN. Servers are normally programmed by the LAN product manufacturer to provide the following functions:

File Server — providing shared disk facilities and sometimes mail-box facilities;

Print Server — providing shared printer operation;

Name Server — used to map user defined names onto network addresses;

Time/Day Server — providing day and time of day facilities using as a timing source a real time clock (battery backed against power failure);

Communications Gateway Server — providing a communications interface to external communications services.

A LAN product manufacturer normally supplies additional equipment for network configuration set-up, network control, network monitoring and fault diagnosis.

IEEE 802 LOCAL AREA NETWORK STANDARDS

The IEEE Local Network Standards Committee (Project 802) in the USA is developing LAN access standards and LAN protocols in a layered approach similar to the ISO Open System Interconnection Reference Model.

Sub-groups within the IEEE 802 committee are producing the following LAN standards:

IEEE 802.1
Part A Overview and Architecture
Part B Addressing, internetworking and network management

IEEE 802.2
Logical Link Control (LLC) common to the various types of media implementation

IEEE 802.3
Carrier Sense Multiple Access and Collision Detection (CSMA/CD) access method and physical layer specifications

IEEE 802.4
Token-Passing Bus access method and physical layer specifications

IEEE 802.5
Token-Passing Ring access method and physical layer specifications

IEEE 802.6

Metropolitan Network access method and physical layer specifications.

The IEEE 802.3 standard with minor differences has been adopted by ECMA as:

ECMA Standard 80

CSMA/CD Baseband LAN — coaxial cable system

ECMA Standard 81

CSMA/CD Baseband LAN — physical layer

ECMA Standard 82

CSMA/CD Baseband LAN — link layer.

ISO has adopted the IEEE LAN standards as ISO 8802.

The IEEE 802 standards are related to each other (as shown in Fig. 9.1) and to the OSI 7-layer model (as shown in Fig. 9.2).

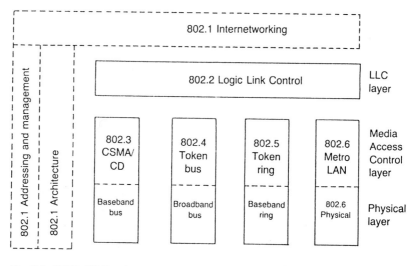

Fig. 9.1. IEEE 802 Standards.

Logical Link Control (LLC)

The IEEE 802.2 Logical Link Control protocol is used in conjunction with each of the four media access standards (802.3, 802.4, 802.5 and 802.6).

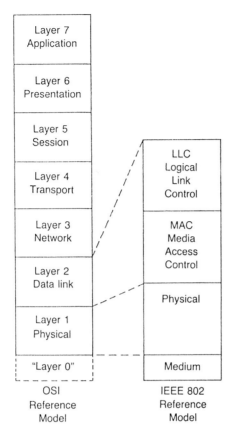

Fig. 9.2. Relationship between IEEE 802 and OSI models.

The LLC protocol handles data in the form of data units. The format of an LLC protocol data unit (L-PDU) is as follows:

1 octet	Destination Service Access Point (DSAP) address;
1 octet	Source Service Access Point (SSAP) address;
1 octet	Control;
N octets	Information.

The control octet has the same format as the single octet control field in an HDLC frame. Information, supervisory and unnumbered frames are supported as in HDLC (see Chapter 15). The Flag and FCS (CRC) fields found in HDLC frames are not used because they are provided by the Media Access Control (MAC) frame.

LLC supports two types of service:

Type 1 connectionless

In type 1 operation, data units are exchanged between stations without the need for the establishment of a logical link. Data units are not acknowledged and there is no flow control nor error recovery.

Type 2 connection orientated

In type 2 operation, a logical link is established prior to any exchange of user data. In the data transfer mode, data units are delivered in sequence. Error recovery and flow control are provided.

These types are grouped in two classes: class 1 supports only the type 1 service and class 2 supports type 1 and type 2 services.

L-PDUs are contained in the information fields of MAC frames and transported between stations on a LAN by the MAC protocol. A MAC frame contains physical LAN addresses and the DSAP and SSAP Addresses in an L-PDU allow one physical connection to be divided into a number of logical channels.

Media Access Control (MAC)

Each of the different IEEE 802 media access methods has a slightly different MAC frame format. The formats are shown in the access method descriptions in Chapters 10 and 11.

Physical Layer

The physical layer defines the physical interface to the medium being used, the generation/detection of signals used on the medium and the conversion/processing of signals between the medium and the media access control (MAC) layer. The function of conversion/processing is performed by the medium attachment unit (MAU), defined in this layer.

OTHER LAN STANDARDS

Purdue Workshop/Proway (TC5A of IEC/SC65A/WG 6) is a standards body defining Local Area Networks for industrial applications (Process Control etc).

DEC/INTEL/XEROX (DIX) is a three-company combine which produced the ETHERNET baseband standard.

The American National Standards Institute (ANSI) X3T9.5 subcommittee is defining Local Area Networks which operate at transmission rates greater than 40 Mbit/s. There are currently two main activities:

Local Distributed Data Interface (LDDI)

This is a 70 Mbit/s coaxial cable network proposed by Digital Equipment Corp. which uses a star topology and an access method which is a form of CSMA/CP (collision prevention).

Fiber (fibre) Distributed Data Interface (FDDI)

This is a 100 Mbit/s fibre-optic ring network which uses a token-passing access method.

The US Department of Defense is developing standards for a low-speed LAN and a fibre-optic based LAN:

MIL-STD 1553 Low speed LAN for harsh environments;

MIL-STD 1773 Fibre-optic bus LAN (draft).

THE CLASSIFICATION OF LANS

LANs are normally classified in terms of:

Broadband or baseband transmission;

LAN topology;

Physical medium used;

Media Access method used;

LAN standards that apply;

Transmission rate on the LAN;

Whether the LAN is "open" (can attach any user device) or "closed" (can attach only specific devices).

The first five of these classifications have been used to produce a LAN classification table (Fig. 9.3). Chapter 10 on Broadband LANs and Chapter 11 on Baseband LANs cover the standards mentioned in the table.

BROADBAND or BASEBAND		MEDIA ACCESS METHODS				
LAN TOPOLOGY	PHYSICAL MEDIUM	CSMA	TOKEN PASSING	EMPTY SLOT	REGISTER INSERTION	ANY OTHER
BROADBAND BUS	Flexible coaxial cables RG-6 RG-11 RG-59	CSMA/CD or CSMA/CA IEEE 802.3 Standard?	IEEE 802.4 TOKEN-BUS STANDARD Non-Directional Bus			
BROADBAND BUS/TREE	CATV Technology semi-rigid and flexible coaxial cables	CSMA/CD or CSMA/CA IEEE 802.3 Standard?	IEEE 802.4 TOKEN-BUS STANDARD Directional Bus			
BASEBAND BUS	Coaxial, twisted pair or multi-wire cable	(Ethernet) IEEE 802.3 CSMA/CD & CHEAPERNET STANDARD [Micro-nets]	Future IEEE Standard? [Micro-nets]			
BASEBAND BUS/STAR	Fibre-optic star coupler and Ethernet coaxial segments	(Ethernet) IEEE 802.3 CSMA/CD				
BASEBAND STAR	Coaxial, twisted pair or fibre-optic cable. Internal bus & RS-232-C	Fibre-optic Ethernet, f-o coupler and special transceivers IEEE 802.3 Standard?				PABX DATA-PBX STDM (DOVE) PSE CSE
BASEBAND STAR/RING	Coaxial, twisted pair or fibre-optic cable		IEEE 802.5 TOKEN RING with central by-pass switching	CAMBRIDGE RING with central by-pass switching		
BASEBAND RING	Coaxial, twisted pair or fibre-optic cable		IEEE 802.5 TOKEN RING STANDARD	CAMBRIDGE RING (CR) STANDARD	Low cost Ring LANs	

Fig. 9.3. LAN classification table.

Chapter 10

Local Area Networks — Broadband

INTRODUCTION

This chapter describes the characteristics of broadband LANs. The IEEE 802.4 Standard divides broadband LANs into non-directional bus and directional bus LANs. The non-directional bus is for small systems and the most basic system uses a single length of unamplified cable. The directional bus is for medium and large systems and uses CATV type technology. The majority of products currently available use the directional bus.

A NON-DIRECTIONAL BUS LAN

Radio frequency (RF) modems are used to transmit and receive data over a broadband LAN.

A basic broadband LAN, as defined in the IEEE 802.4 standard, uses a "non-directional bus" where a single length of flexible coaxial cable connects together a number of stations (see Fig. 10.1). The bandwidth of the cable is divided into two frequency bands (channels). One channel is used for transmission and one channel for reception. Switched RF carrier operation is used to enable one station to send data to another station on the LAN. Prior to data transmission a station switches on its RF modulator carrier and after transmission it switches off its carrier. During data transmission modulated RF signals from the modulator of a transmitting station travel in opposite directions down the LAN cable to the RF demodulators of stations connected to the cable. In the IEEE 802.4 standard this is referred to as "non-directional bus" operation.

The IEEE 802.4 token passing protocol (see broadband media access control) is used to determine which station will send next in any given circumstance. A frame transmitted over the LAN includes source and destination station addresses and each station uses the destination address to identify its own traffic.

This type of broadcast operation can be compared to multipoint operation except that the role of master station passes from station to station.

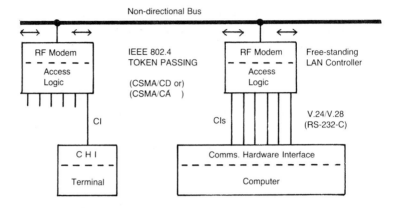

Fig. 10.1. Broadband LAN (non-directional bus).

A DIRECTIONAL BUS (CATV) LAN

A "directional bus" LAN, as defined in the IEEE 802.4 standard, is based on the broadband coaxial distribution system initially developed for Community Antenna Television (CATV) — a cable television company in the USA. This type of LAN uses frequency division multiplexing (FDM) to divide the bandwidth of a broadband cable system into smaller frequency bands called channels, each of which can be used independently. It can use a bandwidth of around 400–550 MHz though experts claim that the technology exists (but is not commercially available) to almost double this bandwidth.

The CATV cable trunk system uses a high quality semi-rigid coaxial cable (normally 1–1.25 cm diameter) as the backbone of the system. The cable system was initially developed as a TV distribution system providing 40+ TV channels. Its topology resembles a tree with the distribution in a direction towards the branches. Branches are formed by splitting one cable run into two, four or eight cable runs. Amplifiers are inserted at regular intervals to boost the cable signals and to compensate for losses incurred in splitting the cable run. The distribution source (cable company) is known as the "head-end" and the TV subscribers are known as "remote ends".

TV subscribers are connected to the cable system by means of passive circuitry contained in a die-cast box known as a "tap".

Taps come in four models to connect one, two, four or eight subscribers to one point on a cable. An individual flexible drop cable (30 m max.) is run from a tap box to each subscriber's television set.

This cable system has been used for many years to provide entire cities with multi-channel television and as a result the associated hardware (taps, splitters and amplifiers) that make up the cable system are mass produced.

Each different TV channel occupies 6 MHz of bandwidth on a cable. The total bandwidth is from 5 to 300/400 MHz. Figure 10.2 shows each CATV channel with its CATV reference and its frequency range within the overall bandwidth. To make the table easier to read, all the frequency range figures are rounded up. For example, Channel 2, which is actually 53.75–59.75 MHz, is shown as 54–60 MHz.

Channel	Frequency Range (MHz)	Channel	Frequency Range (MHz)
T7	6–12	G	156–162
T8	12–18	H	162–168
T9	18–24	I	168–174
T10*	24–30	7	174–180
T11*	30–36	8	180–186
T12*	36–42	9	186–192
T13*	42–48	10	192–198
T14*	48–54	11	198–204
2 *	54–60	12	204–210
3 *	60–66	13	210–216
4 *	66–72	J *	216–222
4A *	72–78	K *	222–228
5 *	78–84	L *	228–234
6 *	84–90	M *	234–240
FM1*	90–96	N *	240–246
FM2	96–102	O *	246–252
FM3	102–108	P *	252–258
A2	108–114	Q *	258–264
A1	114–120	R *	264–270
A	120–126	S *	270–276
B	126–132	T *	276–282
C	132–138	U *	282–288
D	138–144	V	288–294
E	144–150	W	294–300
F	150–156		

Fig. 10.2. CATV Channels. The asterisks indicate the forward and reverse channel pairing for a mid split configuration as recommended by the IEEE 802.4 Standard. For example, reverse channel T10 is paired with forward channel J.

Data Transmission on a CATV Type LAN

Radio-frequency (RF) modems are required to transmit/receive data over a CATV cable system. Modems are attached to "taps" in a similar manner to a TV subscriber by means of flexible coaxial cables. A CATV cable system dedicated to TV distribution only is unsuitable for data communications purposes because it is unidirectional (i.e. suitable for simplex operation only).

To provide half-duplex or full-duplex data operation all CATV type LANs operate as follows. Data from remote ends are carried on reverse channels to the head-end and then on forward channels from the head-end back to all remote ends. This is referred to as "directional bus" operation in the IEEE 802.4 standard.

A broadband CATV type LAN can be implemented in one of two ways.

> Two CATV cable systems can be used, one for data in one direction (forward channels) and one for data in the opposite direction (reverse channels). Signals on the cable are boosted by unidirectional amplifiers. This method requires two coaxial cables and the head-end consists of a physical loop of broadband cable (Fig. 10.3).

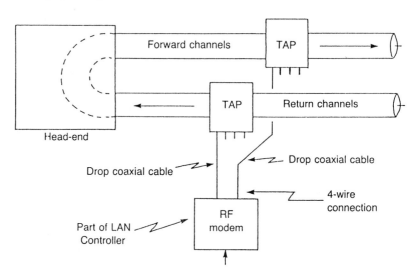

Fig. 10.3. Two cable CATV Broadband LAN.

> A single CATV cable system can be used by dividing the frequency band of the cable into two frequency bands (Fig. 10.4). A return band is used for data transmission from remote ends to the head-end (reverse channels) and a forward band is used for data transmission in the opposite direction, from the head-end to remote ends (forward channels). With this method, bi-directional cable

amplifiers are used in place of unidirectional cable amplifiers. At the head-end an item of equipment known as a Remodulator or Translator is required. It converts the incoming CATV low frequency reverse band to the outgoing CATV high frequency forward band for retransmission along the cable (this conversion can be on an individual CATV channel basis).

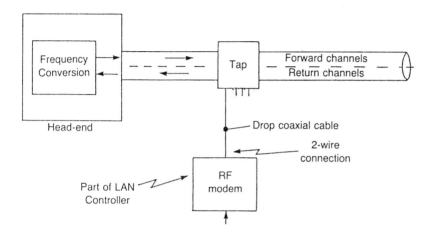

Fig. 10.4. One cable CATV Broadband LAN.

The division of the frequency bandwidth of a single CATV cable system into forward and reverse channels is known as splitting. The exact point in the total bandwidth at which the split occurs varies from manufacturer to manufacturer. There are three main types of split providing different ratios of forward channels to reverse channels.

Sub-split

Total bandwidth of return path around 25 MHz (Inbound to head-end); Total bandwidth of forward path around 350 MHz (Outbound from head-end).

This unequal split is popular with the CATV television industry and is used to support some two-way communications but still allow the distributed television channels to occupy their normal channel assignments.

Mid-split

Total bandwidth of return path around 100 MHz (Inbound); Total bandwidth of forward path around 225 MHz (Outbound).

This is the split normally used for commercial broadband LAN systems. It supports a mixture of data transmission and other applications.

Channels normally used for data transmission are marked with an asterisk on the CATV channel table (see Figure 10.2).

High-split

Total bandwidth of return path and forward path approximately equal at around 170 MHz;

This split is more appropriate to pure data transmission applications.

The single CATV cable system is more popular than the two CATV cable system because it is cheaper to implement. With this method an RF modem transmits on the low frequency band and receives on the high frequency band. If each pair of communicating modems are tuned to a different frequency range within each band then one CATV cable system can support a large number of point-to-point full-duplex links. An RF modem with the ability to operate on one of a number of different frequencies is said to be "frequency agile". If an RF modem and a conventional voice frequency modem are compared on a basis of maximum transmission rate (bit/s) against bandwidth required, then the RF modem is obviously very wasteful on bandwidth. However on a CATV cable system there is more than enough bandwidth and a simple RF modem design is used to minimise production costs.

As an example, using only twelve CATV channels (six forward plus six reverse) the possible number of full-duplex point-to-point RF modem links are as follows:

225 10 kbit/s asynchronous or 9.6 kbit/s synchronous links
      plus
 22 100 kbit/s asynchronous or 96 kbit/s synchronous links

OR

 75 10 kbit/s asynchronous or 9.6 kbit/s synchronous links
      plus
 37 100 kbit/s asynchronous or 96 kbit/s synchronous links.

BROADBAND MEDIA ACCESS CONTROL

Token Passing

With "broadcast token" operation, all stations receive the same transmitted data and a token (data message) passes from station to station in a logically pre-determined sequence giving each station in turn the right to send data. Each station needs to know to which station it will pass on the token (specified when the configuration is set up).

The IEEE 802.4 (ECMA Standard 90) defines a token-passing bus access method and physical layer specification.

The first issue of the physical layer specification applies only to broadband systems. It covers all types of broadband LAN from the basic "non-directional bus" to the "directional bus" (CATV broadband system). The word "bus" in the title of the standard is a little confusing because the topology of a large CATV type system is more like a "tree" than a "bus".

The standard specifies broadband channels for operation with RF modems at transmission rates of 1, 5 or 10 Mbit/s.

The basic non-directional "bus" consisting of an unbranched length of coaxial cable supports a single transmission rate of 1 Mbit/s. The maximum length of the coaxial cable is dependent on the type of cable used; for RG-6 cable the figure is 1600 m.

The IEEE 802.4 token-passing access method (protocol) uses the following frame format on the LAN:

Preamble	= Pattern	(1 or more octets)
SD	= Start Delimiter	(1 octet)
FC	= Frame Control	(1 octet)
DA	= Destination Address	(2 or 6 octets)
SA	= Source Address	(2 or 6 octets)
Data unit	= Information	(0 or more octets)
FCS	= Frame Check Sequence	(4 octets)
ED	= End Delimiter	

Carrier Sense Multiple Access with Collision Detection (CSMA/CD)

In Chapter 11, the baseband bus section describes the IEEE 802.3 Standard: Carrier Sense Multiple Access with Collision Detection (CSMA/CD) access method and physical layer specifications. The IEEE 802.3 standard applies only to baseband bus operation, but it is planned to incorporate broadband bus operation as an alternative medium in the near future.

Many broadband LAN products, including the IBM PC Network, currently support a CSMA/CD access method.

Some LAN products support an alternative CSMA access method known as CSMA/CA where CA stands for collision avoidance.

CONNECTION TO A BROADBAND LAN

A computer/terminal is not connected directly to an RF modem but via a LAN Controller which normally provides the following functions:

Computer/terminal interface;
LAN frame assembly and disassembly;
Data buffering;
RF modem control.

A Controller is normally supplied as a free-standing micro-processor controlled unit with a number of V.24/V.28 (RS-232-C) serial communications interfaces (CIs), each capable of operation at transmission rates up to 19,200 bit/s. The RF modem is normally packaged as part of the Controller unit. Controllers normally support CSMA/CD, CSMA/CA or token-passing access methods on a CATV type LAN (Fig. 10.5). For their connected devices (computer/terminals) they normally provide support for asynchronous and synchronous operation (e.g. CCITT X.25 or IBM BSC 2780/3780/3270). A user of an asynchronous terminal connected to a controller can request connection to a destination on the LAN network. This is performed by a "dialogue" between the controller and the user via his/her terminal.

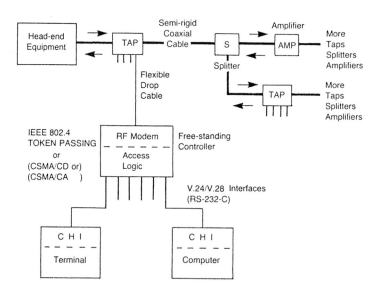

Fig. 10.5. Broadband CATV LAN (directional bus).

One of the advantages of CATV technology is the mixture of services that can be supported on the same cable system. For example, it is possible to have a mixture of point-to-point full-duplex RF modem links, LANs using CSMA and/or token-passing access methods, voice links and Closed Circuit Television (CCTV) links for surveillance and site security purposes.

A single synchronous 9600 bit/s channel can be sub-divided into many low speed asynchronous channels by using standard time division multiplexers.

BROADBAND CABLE

On broadband LANs that use a non-directional bus, the trunk cable is a 75-ohm coaxial cable. Suitable types of cable are flexible coaxial cables RG-59, RG-6 or RG-11 and semi-rigid CATV type cable.

Broadband LAN systems based on CATV technology use semi-rigid coaxial cable for the main trunk and branch routes. Flexible coaxial cable (RG-59, RG-6 or RG-11) is normally used for drops between taps and RF modems; also for the main trunks of small non-branching CATV networks.

Semi-rigid coaxial cable has an unusual construction; beneath the outer plastic cover the outer conductor is a seamless aluminium sleeve instead of the normal woven copper mesh. As a result, this cable is less flexible (minimum bending radius 18 cm) and more expensive than flexible coaxial cable but it does offer higher immunity to electromagnetic and radio-frequency interference.

Chapter 11

Local Area Networks — Baseband

INTRODUCTION

This chapter describes the characteristics of baseband LANs with bus, ring or star topologies. Many LANs use mixed topologies and the following are a few examples:

    Bus/Tree Bus LANs interconnected by repeaters;

    Bus/Star Bus LANs interconnected by fibre-optic star couplers;

    Star/Ring Ring LANs with centralised by-pass switching.

There are a number of low cost baseband bus LANs specifically designed for micro-computer systems and these are referred to as Micro-nets.

Within a baseband LAN all data is transmitted/received over the transmission medium in digital form (modems are not required). For a baseband LAN system this transmission medium can be:

    Coaxial cable;

    Twisted pair cable;

    Fibre-optic cable;

    Multi-wire ribbon/round cable.

The following three baseband LAN Standards are described in this chapter.

LAN Standard	LAN topology	LAN Access Method
IEEE 802.3	BUS	CSMA/CD
IEEE 802.5	RING	TOKEN PASSING
CAMBRIDGE RING (CR83)	RING	EMPTY SLOT

BASEBAND BUS LANS

Ethernet Specification

A baseband bus LAN generally uses a single unamplified section of baseband coaxial cable or a number of cable sections connected together by repeaters to form a large scale network.

150

Ethernet is a baseband bus LAN which has been specified by DIX (DEC, INTEL and XEROX). It is based on single lengths of coaxial cable each up to 500 m long, known as "segments". Connection to the cable is made by using a combined tap and transceiver unit. A transceiver interface cable (nine conductors) connects the transceiver unit to the LAN Controller. The maximum length of a transceiver cable is 50 m (see Fig. 11.1).

The Ethernet specification defines the Ethernet frame format as follows:

32 bits	Preamble — identifies the start of frame
64 bits	Destination Address
64 bits	Source Address
16 bit	Type — network routing instructions
$8 \times N$ bits	Data (N=46−1200)
32 bits	Cyclic Redundancy Check (CRC)

Frame size is 72 octets (576 bits) minimum.

In general, a bus LAN operates using a form of broadcast, where one station sends and all the other stations receive (listen). Digital signals from a station's transceiver propagate along the coaxial cable in both directions to all the other stations.

Ethernet uses a form of bus contention operation known as Carrier Sense Multiple Access with Collision Detection (CSMA/CD). CSMA/CD is based on the characteristics of the ALOHA Network which is a packet radio network developed at the University of Hawaii. The philosophy of CSMA/CD operation is that all stations on the LAN network are equal and a station may attempt to send data to another station whenever it wishes. Obviously, two or more stations can attempt to send at the same time and data packets collide. To overcome this problem each station listens before starting to send to ensure that the LAN bus is idle. A station continues to monitor the bus while sending, to detect collisions should they occur. If a collision is detected, a station continues to send to reinforce the collision (to ensure that all stations detect the collision) and then stops sending. After a collision each station involved waits a random amount of time (determined by a special algorithm) before retrying. This reduces the chance of a second collision. Many LAN product manufacturers are offering baseband and broadband LAN systems based on the use of CSMA/CD operation.

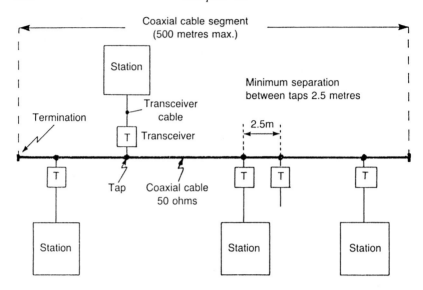

Fig. 11.1. Ethernet (IEEE 802.3) single segment configuration.

IEEE 802.3 Standard

The IEEE 802.3 standard specifies a CSMA/CD access method and physical layer specifications. This standard was based on the Ethernet specification; however, there are about 30 differences between the two documents. One obvious difference is the format of the frames; the IEEE media access control (MAC) frame format is as follows:

$$
\begin{array}{rll}
\text{Preamble} &= \text{Pattern} & \text{(7 octets)}\\
\text{SFD} &= \text{Start of frame delimiter} & \text{(1 octet)}\\
\text{DA} &= \text{Destination Address} & \text{(2 or 6 octets)}\\
\text{SA} &= \text{Source Address} & \text{(2 or 6 octets)}\\
\text{L} &= \text{Length} & \text{(2 octets)}\\
\text{Data unit} &= \text{Information (+ pad bits)} & \text{(46–1500 octets)}\\
\text{FCS} &= \text{Frame check sequence} & \text{(4 octets)}
\end{array}
$$

The IEEE 802.3 subgroup is also considering three other media for use with the CSMA/CD access method.

CSMA/CD with Low Cost Cable System (Cheapernet)

The IEEE 802.3 subgroup has produced a draft standard for a baseband bus LAN using the CSMA/CD access method but with a low cost baseband coaxial cable system. This system is known as "cheapernet" and is intended for small configurations of workstations and personal computers. The low cost is achieved in several ways.

The LAN transmission rate is the same (10 Mbit/s), but thin flexible coaxial cable (RG-58) is used which is lighter and more flexible than standard (Ethernet) thick coaxial cable. A LAN cable section has a maximum length of 200 m (500 m for thick cable) and connects a maximum of 30 nodes with a minimum separation of 0.5 m (100 nodes and 2.5 m for thick cable).

A transceiver of simpler design is integrated into the LAN controller which eliminates the need for transceiver interface cables. LAN controllers are daisy chained together using thin coaxial cable and BNC connectors. A LAN controller normally consists of a single printed circuit board plugged into a micro-computer or personal computer.

CSMA/CD with Broadband Media

As mentioned in Chapter 10, the IEEE 802.3 subgroup is investigating the use of CSMA/CD with broadband media.

CSMA/CD with Optical Fibre Cable Systems

The IEEE 802.3 subgroup is investigating the use of optical fibre cable systems with the CSMA/CD access method for applications that require security or where electrical noise is a problem. The topology will be a star, or multi-star and the optical fibre cable system will require a special medium attachment unit (transceiver equivalent).

Fibre-optic system suppliers are already providing Ethernet or IEEE 802.3 compatible fibre-optic transceivers for use with their passive fibre-optic star couplers (Fig. 11.2). A star coupler is a small free-standing unit fitted with from 4 to 64 fibre-optic ports. Inside the unit there is a passive fibre-optic star where light from any input fibre appears on all the output fibres.

Each fibre-optic transceiver is connected by a transceiver interface cable to its station and by a point-to-point fibre-optic cable to a star coupler. Star couplers can be interconnected by fibre-optic repeaters to form larger networks.

Larger networks are also being constructed by using star couplers and repeaters to connect together standard coaxial cable segments used on Ethernet or IEEE 802.3 networks.

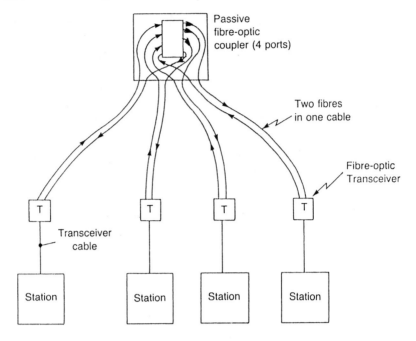

Passive
fibre-optic
coupler (4 ports)

Two fibres
in one cable

Fibre-optic
Transceiver

Transceiver
cable

Station   Station   Station   Station

Fig. 11.2. Ethernet (IEEE 802.3) compatible fibre-optic star configuration.

Token Passing

Token passing can be used with a baseband bus LAN.

The IEEE 802.4 (ECMA 90) Standard mentioned in Chapter 10 specifies a token-passing bus access method and physical layer specifications. At the time of writing, the first physical layer specification agreed for the IEEE 802.4 Standard is for a broadband bus; eventually there should be one for a baseband bus.

Baseband Bus LAN Products

A LAN controller (sometimes called a network interface unit [NIU]) is normally a free-standing unit connected to the main LAN coaxial cable by a transceiver cable and a combined transceiver unit/tap (Fig. 11.3).

An NIU is normally of modular design and each unit provides from four to sixteen V.24/V.28 (RS-232-C) asynchronous or synchronous interfaces for the connection of user devices (computer/terminals).

An NIU generally supports the connection of a printer by an IEEE 488 parallel interface.

For asynchronous operation no special LAN software is required for the computer or terminal systems and the LAN is transparent.

The standard asynchronous software supplied for the NIUs provides a "user friendly" interface for display terminal operation. A user can select and be connected to a destination port (computer) on the LAN. The connection is maintained until the user requests a disconnection.

For synchronous operation, a variety of control character and bit orientated protocols are supported including CCITT X.25.

A baseband bus LAN supports only a single data service and cannot support additional voice or CCTV services.

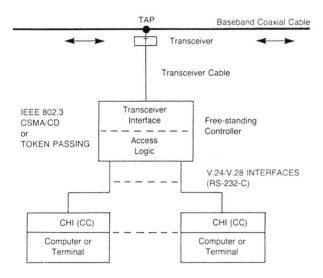

Fig. 11.3. Baseband Bus LAN.

Micro-Nets

There are a number of low cost baseband bus LANs specifically designed to interconnect micro-computer systems. These LANs are often referred to as micro-nets.

In this type of LAN a user device is normally a micro-computer system (personal computer) containing the LAN controller as a plug-in printed circuit board (Fig. 11.4). The interface between the user device and the LAN controller (station) is internal to the micro-computer system and is not accessible. A LAN which does not offer standard communications interfaces for the connection of devices (computer/terminals) is referred to as "closed LAN".

Some LAN product manufacturers provide the entire system including the micro-computer systems and others provide only the LAN medium and controller (PCB).

The length of these LANs is often limited to a few hundred metres and multi-wire ribbon or round cable is often used as the transmission medium.

The LAN access method used is normally based on CSMA/CD or token passing.

One of the major features of micro-nets is the provision of server facilities: file, print, mail-box and communications servers being the most common.

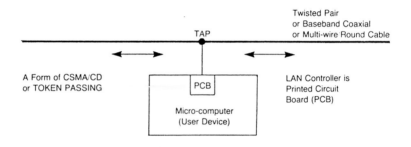

LAN product manufacturer normal supplies user device.
Other devices with attached peripherals are programmed
by manufacturer to provide server functions.

Fig. 11.4. Micro-Net LAN.

BASEBAND RING LANS

Ring Networks

The first ring LAN system in the UK was developed by Cambridge University and is known as the Cambridge Ring.

A ring network (Fig. 11.5) consists of a number of ring "controllers" connected in a ring by point-to-point baseband links. These links may use twisted pair cable, coaxial cable or fibre-optic cable. A ring is unidirectional and packets carrying data circulate around the ring in one direction. A ring controller is usually a free-standing unit consisting of two functional parts, a LAN repeater to regenerate the LAN baseband signals and a device "access logic".

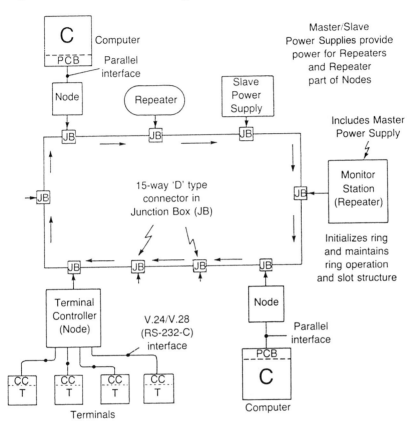

Fig. 11.5. Typical Cambridge Ring System.

With a ring system a device (computer) is normally connected to a ring controller by a parallel interface. In most cases a printed circuit board (PCB) which is device compatible is plugged into the device and this PCB is connected by an interface cable to the "access logic" in the associated ring controller (Fig. 11.6).

LAN ring manufacturers offer a variety of device compatible interfaces, the following interfaces are the most common:

DEC PDP-11 Unibus;

DEC LSI-11 Q-bus;

Intel Multibus (IEEE 796);

S100 bus (IEEE 696).

Terminal concentrators (stations), each with up to 16 asynchronous V.24/V.28 ports, are used to connect asynchronous terminals to a ring.

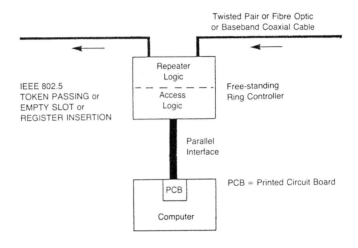

Fig. 11.6. Baseband Ring Controller.

In a simple ring LAN, a cable break affects all stations. To overcome this type of problem, LAN product manufacturers have developed systems with a dual ring capability or with topologies which are a combination of a ring and a star (Fig. 11.7).

Ring Media Access Methods

There are three main strategies for controlling the flow of data between devices on a ring system.

Token Passing Ring (Token Ring)

With this access method the right to send data passes from one station (device) to another station in an ordered sequence by means of a token. A token is a special message which represents permission to send data. When a station receives the token it may send data for some maximum time. When the station has finished sending or if it has nothing to send, it passes on the token to the next station in the sequence.

The IEEE standard 802.5 (ECMA Standard 89) specifies a Token-Passing Ring access method and physical layer specifications.

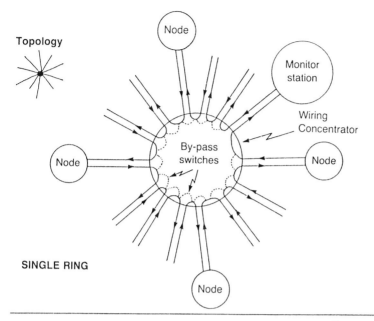

Topology

Node

Monitor
station

Wiring
Concentrator

By-pass
switches

Node

Node

SINGLE RING

Node

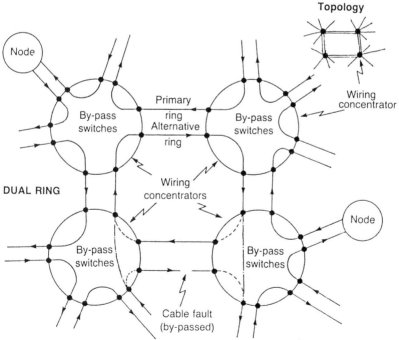

Topology

Node

Primary
ring
Alternative
ring

By-pass
switches

By-pass
switches

Wiring
concentrator

Wiring
concentrators

DUAL RING

By-pass
switches

By-pass
switches

Node

Cable fault
(by-passed)

Fig. 11.7. Star/Ring configurations.

The LAN data signalling rate is 1 Mbit/s or 4 Mbit/s and the maximum number of stations on a ring is 250 (including repeaters).

The standard specifies the following media access control (MAC) frame format for MAC protocol operation on the LAN.

SD =	Starting delimiter	(1 octet)
AC =	Access control	(1 octet)
FC =	Frame control	(1 octet)
DA =	Destination address	(6 octets)
SA =	Source address	(6 octets)
INFO =	Information	(0 or more octets)
FCS =	Frame Check Sequence	(4 octets)
ED =	Ending Delimiter	(1 octet)
FS =	Frame status	(1 octet)

A token is three octets long and consists of SD, AC and ED fields.

Register (Buffer) Insertion

The message to be sent is loaded into a station's First-In First-Out (FIFO) buffer. When the ring becomes idle, or if the end of a message is detected, the ring is broken and the station's buffer is inserted to send the new message onto the ring. The station's buffer must be removed before the station may send again. This access method is used by a number of ring LAN products at the bottom of the price range.

Circulating Empty Slot

With this strategy, a number of empty slots (packets) continuously circulate around the ring. These empty packets are usually initiated at power-up by a monitor station. The monitor station also monitors the ring for errors. When a ring station receives an empty slot (packet) it may send data. If data is to be sent, then two octets of data are inserted in the empty packet and the full/empty indicator in the packet is set to full. The destination station does not delete a packet but instead sets the response bits of the packet which then travels back to the originator (sender) for deletion.

In the UK, the Joint Network Team of the Computer Board for Universities and Research Councils in 1982 produced specifications in conjunction with UK LAN manufacturers. These specifications, under a general title of Cambridge Ring 82 (CR82), define protocols and interfaces for a Cambridge Ring using the empty slot access method.

The CR82 (CR83) specification defines a 40-bit minipacket.

Bit 1	Leader. Slot framing bit	(always "1")
Bit 2	Full/Empty bit	(full = "1")
Bit 3	Monitor bit	
Bits 4–11	Destination Address	
Bits 12–19	Source Address	
Bits 20–27	Data octet No. 1	
Bits 28–35	Data octet No. 0	
Bit 36	Type bit A	
Bit 37	Type bit B	
Bits 38–39	Response Bits	
	11 = Ignored	(set by source)
	10 = Not selected [rejected]	(set by destination)
	01 = Accept [minipacket read]	(set by destination)
	00 = Busy	(set by destination)
Bit 40	Parity bit (even)	

The 8-bit source/destination addresses provide for a maximum of 254 nodes (stations) per ring, each with a unique 8-bit address in the range 1 to 254. A destination address with an 8-bit value of 255 is used for broadcast purposes.

The two "type" bits A and B are used for data transfer control purposes.

The CR82 specification defines two different types of parallel interface used by LAN ring manufacturers, one with a 50-way interface connector and the other with a 100-way interface connector. This parallel interface connects a ring controller to a printed circuit board supplied for insertion in a user device (computer).

The International Standards Organisation (ISO) is working on a standard for Cambridge Ring LANs.

BASEBAND STAR LANS

Star LAN Networks

A star LAN network consists of central switching equipment to which stations or devices (computer/terminals) are connected by point-to-point links. The media used for these links can be coaxial cable, twisted pair cable, fibre-optic cable or multi-wire ribbon/round cable. As mentioned in Chapter 4, data over voice equipment (DOVE) can be used to provide a radial distribution system for a star LAN.

The equipment at the centre of a star LAN can be either passive or active.

Passive Star

A passive star LAN is normally based on the passive fibre-optic star coupler mentioned earlier in this chapter (IEEE 802.3 Standard).

Stations are connected to fibre-optic transceivers which are in turn connected via fibre-optic links to the star coupler (see Fig. 11.2). The transceivers operate using "switched light" operation and light entering the star coupler on any one input fibre appears on all the output fibres.

Active Star

The equipment at the centre of an active star normally provides one port per connected device and has a high-speed port to port switching capability.

It has been stated that one of the characteristics of a LAN is a high data rate on the LAN medium. In an active star LAN the high speed internal busses inside the central equipment equate to the LAN medium. The LAN "medium" is extremely short and therefore ports provided by the central equipment equate to those provided by geographically dispersed LAN controllers (stations) on a bus/ring LAN. An active star LAN normally provides V.24/V.28 (RS-232-C) port interfaces for operation at data rates up to 19,200 bit/s.

Equipments which satisfy these requirements are as follows:

A digital Private Branch Exchange (PBX, PABX, CBX) with data handling capability (a controversial choice because many consider a PBX to be an alternative to a LAN and not a type of LAN);

A Data PBX also known as a data exchange or digital data switching exchange mainly designed for switching data but with voice switching capability;

A computer system which provides high speed switching;

A statistical time division multiplexer system with user switching;

An X.21 circuit switched exchange (CSE);

An X.25 packet switched exchange (PSE).

Passive Star Access Methods

With a passive star, the access method can be CSMA/CD or Token Passing performed by stations (devices) connected to the star.

Active Star Access Methods

A connection through a PBX or Data PBX is selected by keypad entry or by keyboard entry from an attached device (terminal). The connection is made using time-space-time switching.

A connection through a statistical time division multiplexer is selected by keyboard entry (user switching) from an attached device.

An X.21 CSE uses X.21 call procedures to achieve a connection.

An X.25 PSE uses X.25 switched virtual channel (SVC) operation. A connection is initiated by a call request packet from an attached computer/terminal.

Chapter 12

Data Link Protocols — Introduction

INTRODUCTION

This chapter and the three following describe the general principles of operation of data link protocols old and new. Special protocols used on Local Area Networks (LANs) are not covered.

The International Standards Organisation (ISO) has since 1977 been developing standards under the general title of "Open Systems Interconnection" (OSI) to allow the exchange of information between computer/terminals of different manufacturers. The framework for these standards is a 7-layer model described as the "basic reference model for OSI". Layer 2 of this model is the "data link" layer which provides transfer and control of data over communications lines and error correction. The protocols to be described all fit the description of layer 2 but the majority predate the OSI concept of the 7-layer model. The OSI 7-layer model is summarised in Appendix E.

A data link protocol is a procedure used to control the exchange of data between two or more communicating devices over a point-to-point or multipoint (multi-drop) communications link. In general terms the communicating devices can be:

> Two computers communicating over an inhouse/external point-to-point link;

> A computer communicating with a terminal over an inhouse/external point-to-point link;

> A computer communicating with a number of terminals over an inhouse point-to-point/multi-drop link or external point-to-point/multipoint link;

> Two terminals communicating over an inhouse/external point-to-point link.

Communications line protocols can be divided into full-duplex and half-duplex protocols, as shown by Fig. 12.1. A full-duplex protocol can usually operate as a half-duplex protocol but the reverse is not true.

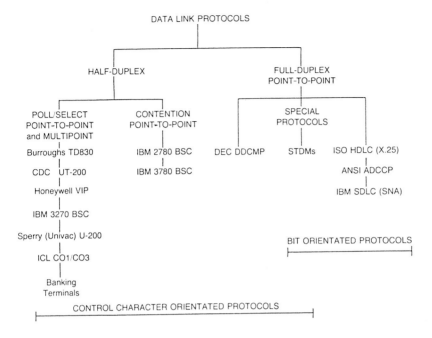

Fig. 12.1. Data Link protocols.

FULL-DUPLEX PROTOCOLS

Full-duplex protocols support the simultaneous transfer of data in both directions (i.e. from device A to device B and from device B to device A) and require a full-duplex point-to-point communications link.

The following are typical examples:

The bit orientated ISO High Level Data-Link Control (HDLC) protocol which is equivalent to the ANSI Advanced Data Communications Control Procedure (ADCCP) protocol;

The bit orientated IBM Synchronous Data Link Control (SDLC) protocol;

The control character orientated DEC Digital Data Communications Message Protocol (DDCMP).

HALF-DUPLEX PROTOCOLS

Half-duplex protocols support the transfer of data in only one direction at a time and can be further sub-divided into "contention" type protocols and "poll/select" type protocols. Contention and poll/select protocols both operate over half-duplex/full-duplex point-to-point links and poll/select protocols can also operate over half-duplex multipoint (in-house multi-drop) links.

Half-Duplex Contention Protocols

The best known are the control character orientated IBM 2780 and the IBM 3780 Remote Job Entry (RJE) protocols.

Half-Duplex Poll/Select Protocols

Most poll/select protocols are used for communicating with clustered display systems and the following control character orientated protocols, of which many are outdated, are the best known:

Burroughs TD 830 protocol
CDC UT-200
Honeywell VIP protocol
IBM 3270 binary synchronous protocol
ICL 7181 (C01) and ICL 7502 (C03) protocols
Sperry (Univac) U-200 protocol.

CHARACTER SETS FOR DATA TRANSMISSION

The early 'sixties saw the introduction of a number of equivalent standards for a 7-bit character set for data transmission:

USASCII (USA Standard Code for Information Interchange) normally abbreviated to ASCII;

CCITT Alphabet No. 5 (International Alphabet No. 5 [IA5]);

ECMA (European Computer Manufacturers Association) 7-bit coded character set.

These standards defined the following set of ten 7-bit transmission control characters:

SOH	Start of Heading
STX	Start of Text
ETB	End of Transmission Block

ETX	End of Text
EOT	End of Transmission
ENQ	Enquiry
ACK	Acknowledgement (positive)
NAK	Negative Acknowledgement
DLE	Data Link Escape
SYN	Synchronous Idle

A control "character" based on a two-character combination was also defined.

DLE EOT	Disconnect Switched Line Connection

TRANSMISSION BLOCK FORMATS

The late 'sixties and the early 'seventies saw the introduction of a number of equivalent protocols (procedures) based on the IA5 (ASCII) 7-bit code. ECMA was the main influence in the UK at that time and UK computer manufacturers (ICL etc) followed the ECMA protocol standards which were called "Basic Mode Control Procedures for Data Communications using the ECMA 7-bit Code". American computer manufacturers (Burroughs, Univac etc) were influenced by the "USA Standard Communications Control Procedures" as defined by the American National Standards Institute (ANSI).

All of these procedures specify the general format of a data transmission block in terms of SYN, SOH, STX, ETB and ETX transmission control characters.

Many of the procedures (protocols) provide both asynchronous and synchronous operation, in the following examples synchronous operation will be shown.

There are two "general" formats for a data block:

A format for the first and intermediate data blocks of a transmission

SYN, SYN, SYN, SYN, SOH, Heading, STX, Text, ETB, BCC

A format for the final data block of transmission

SYN, SYN, SYN, SYN, SOH, Heading, STX, Text, ETX, BCC.

A data block can contain a "start of heading" (SOH) character or a "start of text" (STX) character, or both, and therefore the format of a data block can vary from one manufacturer's protocol to another. A "heading" situated between SOH and STX consists of only a few characters and is normally used for one of the following reasons:

To identify the source of the data block (e.g. terminal identity), with many protocols the identity is contained in the first block of a transmission;

To qualify the contents of the following "text" field as data or status information;

To count each data block for security purposes by incrementing a sequential transmission number count (e.g. 0 to 999).

BLOCK CHECK CHARACTER (BCC)

Error detection for the 7-bit IA5 (ASCII) code is based on an extra character which is added to the end of each transmitted data block. This extra character, which follows the ETB or ETX character, is known as a Block Check Character (BCC) or Longitudinal Redundancy Check (LRC). The BCC character is formed by performing a binary add without carry (alternatively an exclusive OR) on each of the seven bits of the transmitted characters following SOH (or STX if there is no SOH) including ETB or ETX but excluding any SYN characters.

VERTICAL REDUNDANCY CHECK

Each transmitted 7-bit IA5 (ASCII) character has a parity bit (bit 8); this bit is known as the Vertical Redundancy Check (VRC) bit. VRC error checking is the only means of detecting errors in the control character sequences (ACK, NAK, ENQ etc) used in protocols, because only data blocks use BCC error checking.

IBM BINARY SYNCHRONOUS COMMUNICATIONS PROCEDURES

IBM introduced its "Binary Synchronous Communications (BSC) Procedures" which included the 7-bit ASCII code, but not the associated procedures. In fact, IBM uses three character sets in its BSC procedures:

Transcode, a six-bit character set which is now obsolete;

ASCII 7-bit code;

IBM 8-bit EBCDIC (Extended Binary Coded Decimal Interchange Code).

BSC uses nine of the ten ASCII transmission control characters previously defined (the ACK is not used).

In addition, to define further transmission control functions, BSC uses a number of two-character combinations where the first character is a DLE (data link escape). The following is a list of these functions with their equivalent ASCII characters in square brackets:

ACK0 [DLE 0]   Acknowledgement (general purpose ACK plus ACK for even numbered data block)

ACK1 [DLE 1]   Acknowledgement for odd numbered data blocks

RVI   [DLE <]   Reverse interrupt

TTD   [STX ENQ] Temporary text delay

WACK [DLE ;]   Wait-before-transmit positive acknowledgement.

BSC uses an extra transmission control function based on a single character:

ITB   [US]   End of Intermediate Transmission Block.

IBM BSC Transparent Text Mode

BSC specifies a transparent text mode which provides for the transmission of binary data. This mode can only be used with the IBM 8-bit EBCDIC code. Any control characters transmitted in transparent mode must be preceded by a DLE (data-link escape) character if they are to be recognised as control characters.

The following two character combinations are recognised during transparent-text mode operation:

    DLE STX
    DLE ETB
    DLE ETX
    DLE ITB
    DLE ENQ
    DLE SYN.

At the transmitting end an extra DLE is inserted by the CHI for each 8-bit data pattern which resembles a DLE. At the receiving end the CHI removes the first DLE of a pair of characters.

IBM BSC Limited Conversational Mode

BSC has another mode of operation known as "limited conversational mode" which allows a data block to be transmitted in response to a correctly received data block but only if the received block is terminated by ETX or DLE ETX.

When conversational mode is not being used then the normal response to a correctly received data block is either ACK0 (even numbered data block) or ACK1 (odd numbered data block).

IBM BSC Block Check Character

BSC uses two different forms of error checking for the two BSC transmission codes (7-bit ASCII and 8-bit EBCDIC).

> If 7-bit ASCII is used then the BCC at the end of a data block is a single character (Longitudional Redundancy Check [LRC]).

> If 8-bit EBCDIC is used then the BCC at the end of a data block is a 16-bit quantity known as a cyclic redundancy check (CRC) character.

A cyclic redundancy check is a division performed by both the transmitting and receiving devices. The dividend is the numeric binary value of the data block. The divisor is a 16-bit constant (IBM BSC uses hexadecimal C003). The quotient is discarded and the 16-bit remainder is used as the CRC "character".

In a data block all characters following the first SOH or STX up to and including an ETB or ETX (except SYN and the first DLE of a DLE DLE sequence) are included in the CRC calculation.

ASYNCHRONOUS AND SYNCHRONOUS OPERATION

With asynchronous operation each serial character sent/received over an asynchronous modem link or over an inhouse link at 300 bit/s – 19,200 bit/s is normally ten bits long.

One start bit	= "0"
Seven bits	= IA5 (ASCII) code
One parity bit	= odd, even, permanent "0" or permanent "1"
One stop bit	= "1"

The start-stop bits which frame each asynchronous character are used to start and stop the operation of the receiving device. The time between consecutive asynchronous characters can be any value between zero and the specified value of the inter-character time-out period. Time-outs are an important aspect of line protocols. For example, one use of a time-out is to provide a software terminating condition to an unsuccessful or incomplete "read data" operation on a communications link.

With synchronous operation, each character sent/received over a synchronous link at 2400 bit/s – 19,200 bit/s is normally 8 bits long (7 bits IA5 plus a parity bit or 8 bits EBCDIC). The time between consecutive synchronous characters sent as one transmission sequence must be zero.

SYN Characters

When synchronous operation is used in conjunction with a control character orientated protocol, then each transmitted character sequence (data block or response) must be headed by a number of SYN characters. The number of SYN characters prefixing each sequence varies with different protocols and different types of communications link (switched line or leased line). A general rule is to assume a maximum of four SYN characters per transmitted character sequence.

SYN characters are used by the receiving device for character synchronisation purposes. For a receiving device to become character synchronised it must detect two consecutive SYN characters in the received serial character stream. Once synchronised, the remainder of the serial stream is divided into 8-bit quantities and handled as characters, any SYN characters found thereafter being discarded. SYN characters are often found within the data in a data block and these are normally the result of a "SYN fill" operation by the transmitting device.

"SYN fill" is a facility normally performed by a synchronous communications hardware interface (CHI) forming part of a computer/terminal. If a computer which is controlling its synchronous CHI should fail to provide the next character of a transmission sequence in time, then the CHI automatically transmits SYN characters to maintain character synchronisation until the next character is provided. Manufacturers call this a computer "underrun" condition.

On the receiving side there is a reverse situation to this called a computer "overrun" condition. This occurs when a computer cannot accept all the data in a received data sequence from its synchronous CHI because of receive buffer allocation problems. Most CHIs detect this "overrun" condition and inform the computer via status information. In many cases the recovery from an "overrun" condition is to request the data again by sending a NAK. Excessive "underrun" and "overrun" conditions normally point to an overloaded computer system or poor system design.

The main reason for introducing the subject of asynchronous and synchronous operation is to explain that some control character orientated protocols operate equally well with asynchronous or synchronous operation using the same character sequences. For such a protocol the only difference, apart from the number of bits per serial character (10 or 8), is that with synchronous operation each transmitted sequence is preceded by SYN characters.

For bit orientated synchronous protocols (e.g. HDLC, SDLC) the beginning and end of each transmitted sequence (frame) are marked by one 8-bit FLAG character (binary 01111110). SYN characters and control characters are not used and data transmission control functions are provided by a "control" field which is the second character following the leading FLAG in each frame (see Chapter 15).

Chapter 13

Data Link Protocols —Half-Duplex Contention

BASIC PRINCIPLES OF OPERATION

A half-duplex contention protocol is generally used on a point-to-point synchronous link to support the following device configurations:

Computer to computer;
Computer to remote job entry (RJE) terminal;
RJE terminal to RJE terminal.

With a contention protocol, the link is active only when data is being transferred, unlike a poll/select protocol where the communications link is always active due to background polling. When a link which is operating a contention protocol becomes idle then a communications device (computer/terminal) on either end of the link can make a "bid" to use the link and send data. A "bid" on a synchronous link is normally a five character sequence (SYN, SYN, SYN, SYN, ENQ). After sending a "bid" a device waits for an acknowledgement (SYN, SYN, SYN, SYN, "ACK") from the other end which indicates that the "bid" is successful and that the device can proceed to send its data. If a device does not receive an acknowledgement to its "bid" after a given time-out period then the device sends its "bid" again. If two devices on the same link make a simultaneous "bid" then each device will ignore the other's "bid" because with a half-duplex protocol a device is either sending or receiving. To overcome this problem, devices on each end of a communications link have different time-out periods, so that in the case of simultaneous "bidding" one device will eventually win.

A device which has its "bid" acknowledged will start to transmit its data in blocks. Each individual block will be acknowledged (ACKed) or negatively acknowledged (NAKed) by the receiving device and NAKed blocks will be retransmitted by the sending device. Depending on the protocol an "ACK" can be a single ASCII ACK control character, or in the case of IBM's BSC, a two-character combination ACK0 or ACK1. The control character used to terminate the data section of a transmitted block is normally an ETB except for the final data block where an ETX is normally used. When a sending device has sent all of its data blocks it

173

Chapter 13

sends an "end of transmission" sequence (SYN, SYN, SYN, SYN, EOT). The communications link now becomes idle and if the previous receiving device has any data to send it makes a "bid" to use the link. Figure 13.1 shows a typical data transfer operation using a contention protocol.

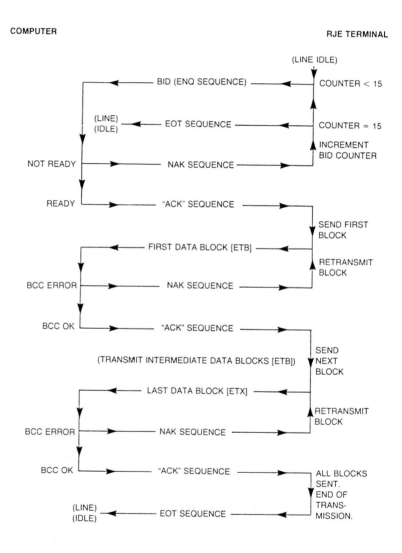

Fig. 13.1. Data transmission using a Contention Protocol.

IBM 2780 CONTENTION PROTOCOL

The IBM 2780 RJE Terminal was introduced by IBM in the late 1960s. The terminal was designed to operate with either a poll/select protocol on multipoint communications links or a contention protocol on point-to-point links. The IBM 2780 contention protocol is the one that is mostly used and the poll/select sequences are not covered. The IBM 2780 contention protocol has become a *de facto* standard for the transfer of bulk data and 2780 emulation is frequently used by devices. The protocol is constrained by the original characteristics of the IBM terminal and these are now considered.

The IBM 2780 RJE Terminal was designed to send large quantities of punched card data to a computer and to receive back large quantities of data for punching or printing. The "component" (printer or card punch) which is to receive the output data can be selected by the computer by means of a two-character address which precedes the data. In IBM terminology this is known as "component selection" and if component selection is not used then the line-printer is selected by default.

Multiple Record Transmission

The following IBM terminology is used to describe the quantity of data sent/received by an IBM 2780 terminal:

Record
The data in a single card or single line of print

Block
A group of one or more records that are transmitted as a unit (block), and which cause a line turnaround (ACK or NAK) to verify the accuracy of the transmission

Message
A group of one or more blocks that represent an entity of data.

The normal method of sending 2780 data is to use "multiple record transmission" where each record can have its own block check character. A block can contain up to seven records but not more than 400 characters, including all format and control characters. This maximum of 400 characters is a constraint based on the size of the hardware communications buffer in the original IBM 2780 terminal.

Characters read from cards by the IBM 2780 card reader are loaded into the communications buffer. Cards which are not fully punched (short cards) have an "end of media" (EM) character punched as the last character. If during card reading an EM character is detected then an "end of record" unit separator (US) character and record BCC characters are inserted in the buffer. If this card is the last record of a "multiple record transmission" then an ETB character is inserted in the buffer instead of a US character. The detection of an EM character completes a card read and blank columns following the EM are ignored.

The format of a multiple record block is:

SYN, SYN, SYN,

STX, RECORD-DATA, US, BCC, STX, RECORD-DATA, US, BCC,

STX, RECORD-DATA, US, BCC, STX, RECORD-DATA, US, BCC,

STX, RECORD-DATA, US, BCC, STX, RECORD-DATA, US, BCC,

STX, RECORD-DATA, ETB (ETX IF LAST BLOCK), BCC.

Reception of an EM character by an IBM 2780 terminal when punching cards causes the punch to feed another card immediately, which results in increased punch throughput. However if the data is being printed then the EM character is ignored. The IBM 2780 terminal has a horizontal tab (HT) feature which allows the remote IBM computer to set up the line printer HT positions. The first record sent by an IBM Computer to an IBM 2780 terminal is usually the "printer horizontal format control record" and this record is stored by the terminal.

Primary/Secondary Device

When an IBM 2780 terminal makes a bid for an idle line then a time period (time-out) of either 1 or 3 seconds is allowed for an acknowledgement.

If the terminal is the "primary device" on the link then the time-out is 1 second; if the terminal is the "secondary device" then the time-out is 3 seconds. When a terminal communicates with an IBM computer then the terminal is the "primary device" and the computer is the "secondary device". This means that the terminal will always win if the terminal and computer make a simultaneous bid. When a terminal communicates with another terminal one must be programmed to be the "primary device" and the other the "secondary device".

Computer or micro-processor systems which provide IBM 2780 emulation are normally programmed as "primary devices". When two such systems (which could be from different manufacturers) are connected to form an RJE terminal to RJE terminal configuration then one system will require its time-out value to be modified to 3 seconds ("secondary device").

Reverse Interrupt (RVI)

A SYN, SYN, SYN, RVI (Reverse Interrupt) character sequence is a positive acknowledgement that is sent instead of an ACK0 or ACK1 sequence by an IBM computer. It is used to terminate a terminal's transmission so that the computer can transmit a high-priority message. The terminal treats the RVI as an ACK and responds by transmitting the remaining record in its buffer which it terminates with an ETX character. When the computer ACKs this record the terminal sends its final EOT sequence. The computer can now bid for the idle line and send its high-priority message.

Wait Before Transmit Positive Acknowledgement (WACK)

A SYN, SYN, SYN, WACK (Wait-Before-Transmit Positive Acknow-ledgement) is a positive acknowledgement that is sent instead of an ACK sequence by an IBM computer. It indicates to the terminal that the computer is not ready to receive further data blocks. The recogni-tion of a WACK sequence by an IBM 2780 terminal causes the terminal to rebid for the line. The IBM computer continues to transmit a WACK sequence in response to each bid until the IBM computer is ready to continue. Normally a terminal stops bidding and sends a final EOT sequence after fifteen consecutive bids have failed to produce a normal ACK0 response. However, the terminal is designed so that each WACK response resets the terminal's "bid" counter.

IBM 3780 CONTENTION PROTOCOL

The IBM 3780 RJE terminal was introduced by IBM in the early 'seventies to provide faster communication, card reading and printing than the IBM 2780. There are many differences between the IBM 3780 and the IBM 2780 contention protocols but the following are the main ones.

Size of Communications Buffer

An IBM 3780 terminal uses a 2×512 character communications buffer and can transmit a data block of up to 512 data characters excluding control characters. (An IBM 2780 terminal is limited to a maximum data block of 400 characters including control characters.)

Conversational Mode

The IBM 3780 provides conversational mode operation which enables a receiving device B on an IBM 3780 link to start data transmission immediately the transmitting device A has sent its last block (terminated by ETX). The first block of the data transmission from B has an implied acknowledgement function and time is saved because the following steps in the contention protocol are not required.

Acknowledgement to last block (sent by B)
EOT sequence to make link idle (sent by A)
Bid sequence (sent by B)
Acknowledgement to bid sequence (sent by A)

Vertical Forms Control

The IBM 3780 provides some additional vertical forms control functions for its printer. The following two-character escape sequences (first two characters in a record) are those for the IBM 3780 printer. (An asterisk indicates the IBM 2780 printer subset.)

ASCII	EBCDIC	Carriage operation	IBM 2780
ESC Q	ESC /	Single Space	*
ESC R	ESC S	Double Space	*
ESC S	ESC T	Triple Space	*
ESC A	ESC A	Skip to Chan 1 (Form Feed)	*
ESC B	ESC B	Skip to Chan 2 (Vertical Tab)	*
ESC C	ESC C	Skip to Chan 3	*
ESC D	ESC D	Skip to Chan 4	*
ESC E	ESC E	Skip to Chan 5	*
ESC F	ESC F	Skip to Chan 6	*
ESC G	ESC G	Skip to Chan 7	*
ESC H	ESC H	Skip to Chan 8	*
ESC I	ESC I	Skip to Chan 9	
ESC J	ESC J	Skip to Chan 10	
ESC K	ESC K	Skip to Chan 11	
ESC L	ESC L	Skip to Chan 12	
ESC M	ESC M	Suppress Space	

Space Compression/Expansion

The IBM 3780 provides space compression whereby two or more space characters found in the card data before transmission are replaced by a two-character combination. The first character of the combination is a group separator (GS) character and the second character is a space count character. On received data, GS characters are deleted and the space-count characters are used to determine the number of space characters to be inserted in the data. (The IBM 2780 has a short card feature (EM character) which is not used by the IBM 3780.)

Chapter 14

Data Link Protocols — Half-Duplex Poll/Select

BASIC PRINCIPLES OF OPERATION

Poll/select protocols are normally used on networks that consist of a computer (master) communicating with a number of terminal devices (slaves) via a point-to-point full/half-duplex link or an external multi-point (internal multi-drop) half-duplex link. A master controls all the data interchanges with its slaves and a slave can transmit data only when requested (polled).

The majority of terminal devices used in poll/select networks are display terminals and printers attached to controllers to form clustered display systems. Polling and selecting are the communications procedures by which a computer (master) receives data from and sends data to its slaves (clustered display systems).

Unlike contention protocols where the character sequences are mainly symmetrical, poll/select protocols are not symmetrical and the character sequences sent by a master to a slave are different from the character sequences sent by a slave to a master. This means that a mini/micro-computer system which emulates a particular manufacturer's clustered display system (e.g. IBM 3270) cannot be connected to another similar system. Therefore there are two types of poll/select protocol emulation:

> Host end emulation;
>
> Terminal end emulation.

A computer system which emulates a "host end" can communicate with another computer system which emulates the corresponding "terminal end". (A "host end" cannot communicate with another "host end" nor a "terminal end" with another "terminal end".)

POLLING

A "poll" is a character sequence sent by a computer to solicit data from a clustered display system. With synchronous operation its maximum

180

length is about 15 characters and the following are examples:

Burroughs poll sequence
SYN,SYN,SYN,SYN,EOT,AD1,AD2,p,ENQ

IBM 3270 poll sequence
SYN,SYN,EOT,PAD,SYN,SYN,AD1,AD1,AD2,AD2,ENQ.

AD1 and AD2 are address characters, AD1 is the cluster controller address and AD2 is the address of a device (VDU or printer) connected to the controller.

On a multipoint link, all cluster controllers see the poll sequence sent by the computer, but they all have different controller addresses (AD1) to which they respond. There are two types of poll: a "specific poll" and a "group (general) poll".

Specific Poll

A "specific poll" is used to solicit data from a specific device (AD2 address) on an addressed cluster (AD1 address).

Group Poll

A "group (general) poll" is used to solicit data from any device on an addressed cluster which has data to send. Where more than one device (e.g. VDU) has data to send then the cluster controller decides which device should send first (round robin priority system). A pseudo AD2 address is used as the means of identifying a "group poll". In the case of the IBM 3270, this AD2 "group" address is 22 (hexadecimal) in ASCII or 7F (hexadecimal) in EBCDIC.

No Traffic Response

After receiving a poll, if the addressed group or specifically addressed device has no data to send then a character sequence (SYN,SYN,SYN, SYN,EOT) is sent back to the computer to indicate that there is "no traffic to send". With poll/select protocols the normal continuous function is polling and in most polled networks a high proportion of polls are answered by "no traffic" responses. These "no traffic" responses have a secondary effect in that they indicate that the communications link and the attached clusters are functioning.

Multipoint Operation

Polling is normally used in conjunction with multipoint circuits and, as described in Chapter 5, there can be from two (minimum) to twelve (maximum) clustered display systems per multipoint circuit (one per spur). The normal method of polling clusters on a multipoint circuit is for the computer to poll each cluster in turn on a round robin basis using "group polls".

Status Polls

Polling is not only used to solicit data, but is also used to solicit status information. This status information can be group status or specific device status. For example, polling is often used to ascertain when a printer (attached to a cluster) has completed the printing of a line so that the computer can send the next line as soon as possible.

Data Transmission

If a device is polled and has data to send, then this data is sent instead of a "no traffic" response. For transmission purposes, the data is normally divided into a number of blocks with the device address contained in the first block. Each block is "ACKed" or NAKed by the computer (master). On receipt of a NAK sequence the cluster retransmits the block in error. When all the blocks have been transmitted and received correctly by the computer, then polling resumes unless there is data to send to a terminal device.

SELECTING

Selecting is the procedure by which the computer sends data to a selected terminal device (VDU or printer).

A "select" is a character sequence sent by the computer to inquire if a selected device can accept data from the computer. The following are examples of a "select" character sequence:

Burroughs select sequence
SYN,SYN,SYN,SYN,EOT,AD1,AD2,q,ENQ

IBM 3270 select sequence
SYN,SYN,EOT,PAD,SYN,SYN,AD1,AD1,AD2,AD2,ENQ.

Comparing the poll and select sequences, it can be seen that Burroughs uses a lower case 'p' to identify a poll and a lower case 'q' to identify a select. The IBM 3270 poll and select sequences are identical and in this case each cluster controller is assigned two cluster addresses (AD1), one for a poll and one for a select. If a terminal device is "not ready" when it receives a select it sends a "NAK" sequence to the computer. However if it is "ready" and can accept the data then it sends an "ACK" sequence to the computer. The computer sends its data, one block at a time, and each block is "ACKed" or NAKed by the terminal device.

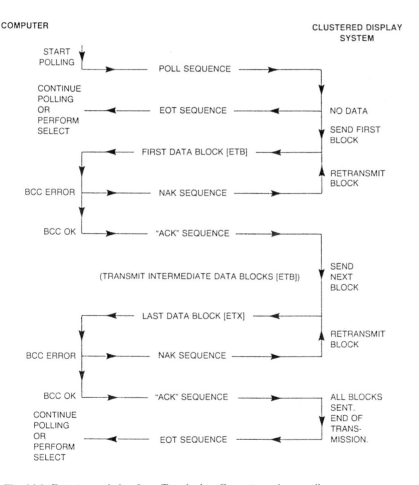

Fig. 14.1. Data transmission from Terminal to Computer using a poll.

In all data transfers, whether to or from the computer, the first and intermediate blocks are terminated by an ETB character and the final block is terminated by an ETX character.

Another form of select is often used where the computer sends the select sequence and the first block of data together as one block. The readiness of the selected terminal device to accept the data is not queried. This is known as a "fast select".

Figures 14.1 and 14.2 show the data transmission sequences for a typical poll and a typical select.

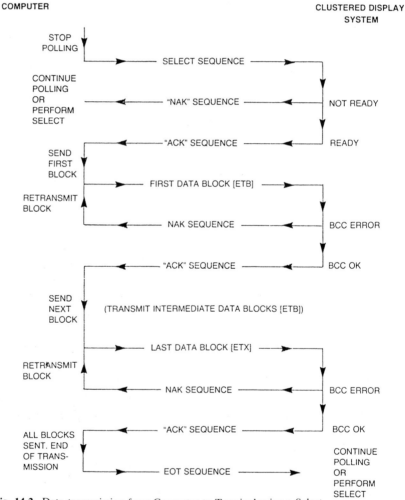

Fig. 14.2. Data transmission from Computer to Terminal using a Select.

Chapter 15

Data Link Protocols — Full-Duplex

INTRODUCTION

The following full-duplex data link protocols are the best known.

The International Standards Organisation's (ISO) High-Level Data Link Control (HDLC) is a bit orientated protocol and is directly equivalent to the American National Standards Institute's (ANSI) Advanced Data Communications Control Procedures (ADCCP). A subset of HDLC is used as the line protocol for CCITT X.25.

IBM's Synchronous Data Link Control (SDLC) is a bit orientated protocol and has a similar frame format to HDLC. SDLC is the line protocol used for IBM's System Network Architecture (SNA).

Digital Equipment Corporation's Digital Data Communications Message Protocol (DDCMP) is the line protocol used for DECNET and is an "unusual" full-duplex protocol because it is control character orientated.

Full-duplex protocols require a full-duplex point-to-point link. They all use a form of piggy-back operation for acknowledgements (ACKs). ACKs to correctly received (incoming) data blocks are transmitted as a field in outgoing data blocks. When there is no data to send then acknowledgements are sent separately in non-data blocks. To avoid any ambiguity as to which data blocks are being acknowledged, each transmitted data block contains a "send sequence count" (Ns) of three bits (counts 0–7). Some full-duplex protocols provide an "extended send sequence count" capability of seven bits (counts 0–127).

For each data block transmitted, the "send sequence count" (Ns) is incremented. The count is circular and the next count after 7 (or 127) is 0.

An acknowledgement is transmitted as a "receive sequence count" (Nr) field in a block. Nr will be equal to Ns+1, where Ns is the send sequence count of the last data block correctly received. All data blocks received up to that sequence count are acknowledged.

So far the term "block" has been used. However, when discussing HDLC/SDLC protocols, the correct term is "frame" (i.e. block equals frame).

HDLC FRAME STRUCTURE

The frame structure for the High-Level Data Link Control (HDLC) protocol is specified in the British Standard 5397 (ISO 3309, ECMA 40) documents as follows:

FLAG	ADDRESS	CONTROL	INFORMATION	FCS	FLAG
8 bits	8 bits	8/16 bits	N bits	16 bits	8 bits

This is the "long" frame format and there is also a "short" frame format which is identical except that it does not have an information field.

Error checking on frames is achieved by the use of a frame checking sequence (FCS) which is generated using the CCITT V.41 CRC-16 polynomial. The CCITT CRC-16 is a different polynomial from the IBM CRC-16 used in Binary Synchronous operation. For HDLC operation, a cyclic redundancy check is a division performed by both the transmitting and receiving devices. The dividend is the numeric binary value of the Address field, Control field and Information field (when present). The divisor is a 16-bit constant (CCITT CRC-16). The quotient is discarded and the remainder is used as the frame checking sequence, i.e. CRC character.

It should now be realised that one of the advantages of HDLC is that all transmissions (data and non-data) use frames and are therefore protected by a CRC check.

HDLC FLAG/ABORT BIT PATTERNS

HDLC is a bit orientated protocol and two bit patterns are used for basic transmission control purposes.

A bit pattern of 01111110 is called a "flag" and is used to mark the beginning and end of each frame.

A bit pattern of from seven to fifteen consecutive ones is an "abort" function and is used by the transmitting device to abort a frame which it has started to transmit.

HDLC ZERO BIT INSERTION/DELETION

Transparency of the data in the address, control and information fields of an HDLC frame is achieved by a technique which is known as "zero bit insertion/deletion" (bit stuffing/unstuffing). Zero bit insertion is performed at the transmitting end and zero bit deletion is performed at the receiving end. The transmitting end inserts an extra zero into the transmit serial stream if it detects a 6-bit serial pattern of 011111; because the next two serial bits could be 10 (a pseudo "flag") or 11 (a pseudo "abort" function). The receiving end performs the reverse operation and deletes the final zero on any received serial pattern of 0111110.

At the transmitting end, genuine "flag" and "abort" bit patterns bypass the zero bit insertion circuitry and are therefore uniquely identified at the receiving end. Zero bit insertion/deletion is a function of a bit orientated synchronous communications hardware interface (CHI).

COMMUNICATIONS HARDWARE INTERFACE FUNCTIONS FOR HDLC AND IBM BSC

The following comparison table shows the different functions performed by a communications hardware interface when handling bit orientated HDLC/SDLC protocols and character orientated IBM BSC protocols.

	HDLC Interface	IBM BSC Interface (using EBCDIC)
Character Synchronisation	Leading FLAG	Two SYN characters
Text Transparency	Bit Insertion/ Deletion	DLE-STX, DLE-ETX etc.
CRC Generation/Checking	From leading FLAG to end of Information field using CCITT CRC-16	From SOH or STX to ETB or ETX using IBM CRC-16.
Detection of End of Frame/Block	Ending FLAG, CRC is two previous characters	ETB or ETX, CRC is two following characters
Abort Frame	7–15 ones	Not provided

Some computer manufacturers provide separate communications hardware interfaces for HDLC and BSC operation and others provide an interface capable of either operation.

HDLC CONTROL FIELD

The key to HDLC operation lies in the coding of the 8 bits of the control field.

Information Frame

For an information (long) frame, the 8 bits of the control field are interpreted as follows.

Bit 1	$= 0$	Indicates that this frame is an information (I) frame
Bits 2,3,4	$= Ns$	Send Sequence Count (modulo 8) (Identifies this I frame)
Bit 5	$= P/F$	Poll/final bit
Bits 6,7,8	$= Nr$	Receive Sequence Count (modulo 8) (Acknowledgement of received frames up to $Nr-1$)

Supervisory Frame

For a Supervisory (short) frame, the 8 bits of the control field are interpreted as follows.

Bits 1,2	$= 10$	Indicates that this frame is a supervisory (short) frame
Bits 3,4	$= S$	Supervisory Functions bits
0 0	$=$	Receive Ready (RR)
0 1	$=$	Reject (REJ)
1 0	$=$	Receive Not Ready (RNR)
1 1	$=$	Selective Reject (SREJ)
Bit 5	$= P/F$	Poll/final bit
Bits 6,7,8	$= Nr$	Receive Sequence Count (modulo 8)

Unnumbered Frame

For an unnumbered frame, the 8 bits of the control field are interpreted as follows.

Bits 1,2	$= 11$	Indicates that this frame is an unnumbered frame

Bit 5   = P/F   Poll/final bit

Bits 3,4,6,7,8 = M   Modifier-function bits

Unnumbered Commands

1 1 0 0 0   Set Asynchronous Response Mode (SARM)

1 1 0 1 0   Set Asynchronous Response Mode Extended (SARME)

1 1 0 0 1   Set Normal Response Mode (SNRM)

1 1 0 1 1   Set Normal Response Mode Extended (SNRME)

1 1 1 0 0   Set Asynchronous Balanced Mode (SABM)

1 1 1 1 0   Set Asynchronous Balanced Mode Extended (SABME)

1 1 0 0 1   Reset (RSET)

1 0 0 0 1   Frame Reject (FRMR)

0 0 0 1 0   Disconnect (DISC)

Unnumbered Responses

0 0 1 1 0   Unnumbered Acknowledge (UA)

1 0 0 0 1   Command Reject (CMDR)

1 0 0 0 1   Frame Reject (FRMR)

The term "extended" means extended send and receive sequence counts 0–127, i.e. modulo 128. For extended sequence count operation, N_s and N_r are both increased from 3 bits (modulo 8) to 5 bits (modulo 128) and as a result the control field is increased from one octet to two octets.

The above list includes the most widely used HDLC unnumbered commands and responses. However it should be noted that there are many more optional extensions to this list of unnumbered commands and responses.

SUMMARY OF HDLC FRAME TYPES

An HDLC frame can be one of four main types:

Information Frame;

Supervisory Frame;

Unnumbered Command Frame;

Unnumbered Response Frame.

Before describing how these frames are used for HDLC operation, is is necesssary to explain the following HDLC concepts.

HDLC STATIONS

HDLC has its own terminology and a communicating device connected to one end of an HDLC communications link is called a "station". Stations can be of three types:

Primary stations which send commands, receive responses and are fully responsible for link level error recovery;

Secondary stations which receive commands, send responses and may participate in error recovery actions;

Combined stations which send both commands and responses and also receive both commands and responses and are equally responsible for link level error recovery.

Any coupling of primary and secondary stations can be operated over any type of transmission link to build unbalanced point-to-point or multipoint configurations. These stations may be operated in the Normal Response Mode (NRM) or the Asynchronous Response Mode (ARM). (NRM and ARM are explained later in section headed HDLC Operational Modes).

Balanced point-to-point systems can be formed in one of two ways.

A symmetrical procedure can be constructed by superimposing two unbalanced procedures in such a way that each end of the link has a primary and a secondary station.

Two combined stations can be used, in which case the stations will operate in the Asynchronous Balanced Mode (ABM).

CLASSES OF HDLC PROCEDURES

There are a number of classes of HDLC procedure and these classes are composed of:

Three types of stations: primary stations, secondary stations and combined stations;

Three types of data flow: data collection, data dissemination, or both; where information (I) frames flow from secondary to primary only, from primary to secondary only, or in both directions;

Two types of transmission response: normal and asynchronous (to be explained);

Three types of configurations: unbalanced (for primary and secondary station), symmetrical (for superimposed primary and secondary station), and balanced (for combined stations);

Two sizes of modulus: 8 and 128 for sequence counts.

These classes of procedure are summarised in the following table.

Designation	Class of Procedure
UAB	Unbalanced operation, Asynchronous Response Mode, Modulo 8
UAE	Unbalanced operation, Asynchronous Response Mode, Modulo 128
UNB	Unbalanced operation, Normal Response Mode, Modulo 8
UNE	Unbalanced operation, Normal Response Mode, Modulo 128
SAB	Symmetrical operation, Asynchronous Response Mode, Modulo 8
SAE	Symmetrical operation, Asynchronous Response Mode, Modulo 128
SNB	Symmetrical operation, Normal Response Mode, Modulo 8
SNE	Symmetrical operation, Normal Response Mode, Modulo 128
BAB	Balanced operation, Asynchronous Response Mode, Modulo 8
BAE	Balanced Operation, Asynchronous Response Mode, Modulo 128

Classes UAB, UAE, UNB and UNE can be used in unbalanced configurations.

Classes SAB, SAE, SNB and SNE can be used in symmetrical configurations.

Classes BAB and BAE can be used in balanced configurations (ABM).

LINK START-UP USING HDLC FRAMES

At system start-up, an unnumbered command frame is transmitted to initiate an HDLC link into a particular mode of operation. At the receiving end a valid command contained in an error free frame is acknowledged by sending back an unnumbered acknowledge (UA) frame. An invalid command contained in an error free frame is rejected by sending back a command reject (CMDR) frame.

An unnumbered command frame (SNRM, SARM or SABM) is used to set an HDLC link into one of three possible modes of operation.

HDLC OPERATIONAL MODES

Normal Response Mode (NRM)

Normal Response Mode is an operational mode in which the secondary may initiate transmission only as the result of receiving explicit permission to do so from the primary. After receiving permission, the secondary initiates a response transmission. The response transmission may consist of one or more frames while maintaining an active channel state. The last frame of the response transmission is indicated explicitly by the secondary. Following the indication of the last frame, the secondary stops transmitting until explicit permission is again received from the primary.

This mode provides poll/fast-select half-duplex operation over point-to-point or multipoint communications links. Operation is based on a master (computer) controlling a number of slaves (terminals) and the address field of an HDLC frame is used to address the slaves.

The poll/final (P/F) bit in the control field of a frame is used by a master to identify a poll and is used by a slave to mark the final frame of a data transmission (equivalent to ETX). A master polls a slave to solicit data by transmitting a Receive Ready (RR) supervisory frame with the address field set to the slave's address and the "poll" (P/F) bit set. The addressed slave transmits its data to the master in information frames and marks the last frame of the transmission by setting the "final" (P/F) bit in that frame.

The master sends its data in information frames to a slave, with the address field set to the address of the slave. The final information frame of the master's transmission is marked by setting the "final" bit in the control field (i.e. the P/F bit). In terms of control character protocols this type of operation can be equated to a "fast-select".

Asynchronous Response Mode (ARM)

ARM is an operational mode in which the secondary may initiate transmission without receiving explicit permission from the primary.

Such an asynchronous transmission may contain single or multiple frames and is used for information field transfer and/or to indicate status changes in the secondary (for example, the number of the next expected frame; transition from a ready to a busy condition or vice-versa; occurrence of an exception condition).

This mode provides full-duplex operation over a full-duplex point-to-point link. Each end of a link can be considered as consisting of a primary station and/or a secondary station.

Note that the word "asynchronous" in this context means "not synchronised" and is not to be confused with the everyday use of the word "asynchronous" used to describe start-stop data transmission.

Asynchronous Balanced Mode (ABM)

ABM is a balanced configuration operational mode in which a combined station may send commands at any time and may initiate frame transmission without receiving permission from the other combined station. Commands are transmitted with the remote station address while responses are transmitted with the local station address.

This mode provides full-duplex operation over a full-duplex point-to-point link. Each end of a link is a combined (primary/secondary) station.

ARM (symmetrical operation) and ABM are used on British Telecom's X.25 Packet Switched Service and are called Link Access Procedure (LAP) and Link Access Procedure Balanced (LAPB) respectively.

OPERATION OF HDLC SUPERVISORY FRAMES

The functions performed by supervisory frames (RR, RNR, REJ and SREJ) will now be described assuming station A connected to station B by a point-to-point link.

Receive Not Ready Frame

A Receive Not Ready (RNR) supervisory frame is sent by station A to inhibit the transmission of information (I) frames by station B. Supervisory frames transmitted by station B are not inhibited and are used to acknowledge and reject information frames sent by station A. This inhibit on the transmission of I frames by station B persists until it is removed by station A sending a Receive Ready (RR) supervisory frame.

The RNR/RR frames provide a flow control mechanism for handling receive buffer overload conditions.

Receive Ready Frame

The Receive Ready (RR) supervisory frame performs a number of functions.

An RR frame with the poll (P/F) bit set is used as a poll sequence when Normal Response Mode (NRM) is being used.

Received frames are normally acknowledged using the Nr field in a transmitted information (I) frame. If there are no information frames to transmit, an acknowledgement is sent in the Nr field of an RR frame. The transmission of information frames stops when there is no data to send or when they have been inhibited by the reception of a RNR frame.

An RR frame is transmitted to remove the data inhibit condition set up by an earlier transmission of an RNR frame.

Reject Frame

The receive sequence count (Nr) field in a Reject (REJ) supervisory frame transmitted to station B, indicates that all frames received by station A starting at Ns=Nr have been rejected. The reception of a REJ frame by station B causes it to retransmit the rejected frames.

Selective Reject Frame

The Selective Reject (SREJ) supervisory frame is an optional supervisory frame which is not used in X.25 operation. It rejects a single frame Nr and requests its retransmission.

The REJ and SREJ supervisory frames also have an implied acknowledgement function in that frames up to and including Nr−1 are acknowledged.

SYNCHRONOUS DATA LINK CONTROL

The frame format for IBM's SDLC is virtually identical to the frame format for HDLC.

The main differences between SDLC and HDLC are as follows.

The information field in an SDLC frame must be an integral number of octets (bytes).

The option of using an extended control field to provide sequence counts of 0–127 (modulo 128) is not provided by SDLC.

The optional Selective Reject (SREJ) supervisory function provided in HDLC is not provided by SDLC.

There are differences between SDLC and HDLC in the number of Unnumbered Commands and Command Responses and their functions.

SDLC has been designed to operate with IBM Loop Configurations. HDLC has not been designed to support this type of configuration.

Chapter 16

Network Configurations

INTRODUCTION

This chapter covers the general principles involved in matching the characteristics of three of the many components used to form a practical network configuration.

To operate a data link protocol over a communications link there must be compatibility between the following:

The selected data link protocol

A computer/terminal implements a protocol using a combination of communications software functions and hardware functions performed by its communications hardware interface (CHI).

The communications hardware interfaces

The CHIs at each end of a link have to match the requirements of the selected data link protocol and the network components.

The communications link

The link can be analogue or digital and must match the characteristics of the CHIs connected to the network and those of the selected data link protocol (full-duplex, half-duplex, point-to-point, multipoint).

There are many different theoretical configurations that can be designed from permutations of these three components. However, in practice, the majority of simple network configurations are satisfied by a number of "standard" arrangements. For each of the three components some simple "standard" configurations are shown and matched for compatibility in a configuration table.

COMMUNICATIONS LINE PROTOCOLS

The list of "standard" communications line protocols is:

    Asynchronous visual display terminal protocols [A-VDT];

    Asynchronous poll/select protocols [A-PS];

    Asynchronous contention protocols [A-C];

Synchronous poll/select protocols [S-PS];

Synchronous contention protocols [S-C];

Synchronous full-duplex bit orientated protocols [S-FB];

Synchronous half-duplex bit orientated protocols [S-HB];

Synchronous full-duplex character orientated protocols [S-FC].

The following are examples of the last three protocols on the list:

S-FB = HDLC Asynchronous Response Mode or HDLC Asynchronous Balanced Mode.

S-HB = HDLC Normal Response Mode.

S-FC = DEC DDCMP.

One "protocol" on the list which has not been previously discussed is the asynchronous character/block mode VDT (A-VDT) protocol, a description used in this book. This protocol is primitive and is not a true data link protocol because it does not have any retransmission on error capability.

ANSI X3.64 standard for VDTs, "Additional controls for use with American National Standard Code for Information Interchange" (ASCII), was approved in 1979. It specifies control character sequences for use by asynchronous VDTs. Digital Equipment Corporation (DEC) adopted the standard for its character mode VT-100 VDT. A later model, the VT-131 VDT, operates in character/block mode. The "protocols" used by these two VDTs are examples of an A-VDT protocol.

Asynchronous VDTs at remote locations normally use statistical multiplexer links for connection to a computer. The multiplexers provide the required retransmission on error protocol (normally HDLC).

COMMUNICATIONS HARDWARE INTERFACES

Each computer/terminal manufacturer normally supplies and supports a range of CHIs. These vary from manufacturer to manufacturer. As described in Chapter 2, a CHI is a hardware item that forms part of a computer/terminal and performs some data link protocol functions. It connects to and controls the DTE side of communications interfaces (CIs).

Most CHIs can be classified into the following general types A to I.

Type A
Asynchronous
Current loop interface
Teletype protocol (A-VDT) on inhouse point-to-point link

Type B
Asynchronous
Special interface using daisy chain cable
Manufacturers' own poll/select protocol (A-PS) on inhouse multi-drop
    link

Type C
Asynchronous
V.24/V.28 (RS-232-C) interface
Teletype protocol (A-VDT) on inhouse point-to-point link
Teletype protocol (A-VDT) on remote point-to-point link (statistical
    multiplexer link preferred)
Contention protocol (A-C) on inhouse or remote point-to-point link
Poll/select protocol (A-PS) on inhouse/remote point-to-point or multi-
    point (multi-drop) link

Type D
Synchronous
V.24/V.28 (RS-232-C) interface
Control character orientated protocols
Contention protocol (S-C) on inhouse or remote point-to-point link
Poll/select protocol (S-PS) on inhouse/remote point-to-point or multi-
    point (multi-drop) link

Type E
Synchronous
V.24/V.28 (RS-232-C) interface
Bit orientated protocols
Full-duplex protocol [S-FB] such as HDLC or SDLC on inhouse/remote
    full-duplex point-to-point link
Half-duplex protocol [S-HB] such as HDLC (normal response mode) on
    inhouse/remote point-to-point or multipoint (multi-drop) link

Type F
Synchronous high speed (up to 168 kbit/s)
V.35 interface (X.21 bis)
Control character orientated protocols
Contention protocol [S-C] on inhouse/external point-to-point link

Type G
Synchronous high speed (up to 168 kbit/s)
V.35 interface (X.21 bis)
Bit orientated protocols
Full-duplex protocol [S-FB] such as HDLC or SDLC on inhouse/remote
full-duplex point-to-point link

Type H
Synchronous medium/high speed (up to 64 kbits/s)
X.21 interface
Control character orientated protocols
Point-to-point link

Type I
Synchronous medium/high speed (up to 64 kbits/s)
X.21 interface
Bit orientated protocols
Point-to-point link

Some computer manufacturers provide CHIs which perform the dual functions of Type D and Type E, Type F and Type G or Type H and Type I. In these CHIs, control character or bit orientated operation is selected by hardware straps, DIP switches or by software set-up.

The Type D, Type F and Type H CHIs are selected by hardware straps, DIP switches or by software set-up to operate with either IA5 (ASCII) or EBCDIC code. Once selected the CHI performs BCC generation/checking based on LRC for ASCII code or the IBM CRC for EBCDIC code. These CHIs automatically generate and detect SYN characters used to mark the beginning of each synchronous transmission.

COMMUNICATIONS LINKS

Communications links can be divided into seven "standard" types:

Type 1, asynchronous, half-duplex, point-to-point;

Type 2, asynchronous, half-duplex, multipoint (multi-drop);

Type 3, asynchronous, full-duplex, point-to-point;

Type 4, synchronous, half-duplex, point-to-point;

Type 5, synchronous, half-duplex, multipoint (multi-drop);

Type 6, synchronous, full-duplex, point-to-point;

Type 7, high speed synchronous, full-duplex, point-to-point.

CONFIGURATION TABLE

The following table matches the characteristics of the protocol to the CHI type and the link type.

Protocol	CHI type	LINK type
A-VDT	A, C	1, 3
A-PS	B, C	1, 2, 3
A-C	C	1, 3
S-PS	D, [F], [H]	4, 5, 6 [7]
S-C	D, F, [H]	4, 6, 7
S-FB	E, G, I	6, 7
S-HB	E, G, I	4, 5, 6 [7]
S-FC	D, F, H	6, 7

CHI or LINK types shown in brackets are possible but highly unlikely forms of configuration.

There are some essential points to remember when matching a protocol to a link.

An inhouse multi-drop link or external multipoint link is capable of only half-duplex link operation.

A full-duplex link is a point-to-point link.

High speed synchronous links are provided only as point-to-point full-duplex links.

A full-duplex protocol requires a full-duplex link.

Contention protocols operate only over point-to-point links.

Synchronous poll/select protocols or full-duplex protocols operating in half-duplex mode (e.g. HDLC NRM) are the only protocols that operate with synchronous multipoint (multi-drop) links.

Asynchronous poll/select protocols are the only protocols that operate with asynchronous multipoint (multi-drop) links (e.g. CHI Type B).

Polling statistical multiplexers operate over synchronous multipoint links and allow asynchronous terminals using a VDT protocol [A-VDT] to be connected at remote outstation locations. Each terminal at a remote location requires one asynchronous CI (CHI port) at the computer centre.

Appendix A

CCITT V-SERIES RECOMMENDATIONS

The CCITT (Consultative Committee for International Telegraph and Telephone) in Geneva Switzerland is a part of the ITU (International Telecommunications Union). The CCITT V-Series recommendations cover data transmission over the telephone network.

V.1 Equivalence between binary notation symbols and the significant conditions of a two condition code

V.2 Power levels for data transmission over telephone lines

V.3 International Alphabet No. 5 (IA5)

V.4 General structure of signals of international alphabet No. 5 code for data transmission over public telephone network

V.5 Standardisation of data signalling rates for synchronous data transmission in the general switched telephone network

V.6 Standardisation of data signalling rates for synchronous data transmission on leased telephone-type circuits

V.7 Definitions of terms concerning data communication over the telephone network

V.10 Electrical characteristics for unbalanced double-current interchange circuits for general use with integrated circuit equipment in the field of data communications

V.11 Electrical characteristics for balanced double-current interchange circuits for general use with integrated circuit equipment in the field of data communications

V.15 Use of acoustic coupling for data transmission

V.16 Medical analogue data transmission modem

V.19 Modems for parallel data transmission using telephone signalling frequencies

V.20 Parallel data transmission modems standardised for universal use in the general switched telephone network

V.21 200 (300) bits per second modem standardised for use on the general switched telephone network

V.22 1200 bits per second duplex modem standardised for use on the general switched telephone network and on leased circuits

V.22 bis	2400 bits per second duplex modem using the frequency division technique standardised for use on the general switched telephone network
V.23	600/1200 bits per second modem standardised for use on the general switched telephone network
V.24	List of definitions for interchange circuits between data terminal equipment and data circuit-terminating equipment
V.25	Automatic calling and/or answering equipment on the general switched telephone network including disabling of echo-suppressors on manually established calls
V.25 bis	Automatic calling and/or answering equipment on the general switched telephone network using the 100 series interchange circuits
V.26	2400 bits per second modem standardised for use on 4-wire leased telephone type circuits
V.26 bis	2400/1200 bits per second modem standardised for use in the general switched telephone network (PSTN)
V.26 ter	2400 bits per second duplex modem using the echo cancellation technique standardised for use on the general switched telephone network and on point-to-point 2-wire leased telephone type circuits
V.27	4800 bits per second modem with manual equaliser standardised for use on leased telephone type circuits
V.27 bis	4800 bit per second modem with automatic equaliser standardised for use on leased telephone type circuits
V.27 ter	4800/2400 bits per second modem standardised for use in the general switched telephone network
V.28	Electrical characteristics for unbalanced double-current interchange circuits
V.29	9600 bits per second modem standardised for use on leased telephone circuits
V.31	Electrical characteristics for single-current interchange circuits controlled by contact closure
V.32	A family of 2-wire duplex modems operating at data signalling rates up to 9600 bits per second for use on the general switched telephone network and on 2-wire leased telephone type circuits
V.35	Data transmission at 48 kilobits per second using 60–108 kHz group band circuits
V.36	Modems for synchronous data transmission using 60–108 kHz group band circuits
V.37	Synchronous data transmission at a data signalling rate higher than 72 kilobits per second using 60–108 kHz group band circuits
V.40	Error indication with electro-magnetic equipment
V.41	Code-independent error-control system
V.50	Standard limit for transmission quality of data transmission

V.51	Organisation of the maintenance of international telephone type circuits used for data transmission
V.52	Characteristics of distortion and error-rate measuring apparatus for data transmission
V.53	Limits for the maintenance of telephone type circuits used for data transmission
V.54	Loop test devices for modems
V.55	Specifications for an impulsive noise measuring instrument for telephone type circuits
V.56	Comparative tests of modems for use over telephone type circuits
V.57	Comprehensive data test set for high signalling rates

V-SERIES RECOMMENDATIONS — ASYNCHRONOUS ONLY MODEMS

V.21 Recommendation

"200 bit/s modem standardised for use in the general switched telephone network"

A V.21 modem is an asynchronous only modem capable of up to 300 bit/s full-duplex operation over a leased/switched 2-wire circuit. A form of frequency modulation is used which is known as Frequency Shift Keying (FSK). This modem was introduced into the UK in the mid-'sixties and was the first modem capable of full-duplex 2-wire operation. It was initially used on the PSTN for remote terminal access to time-sharing systems. It uses "originate/answer" modes of working, where an "originate" modem uses channel A to send and channel B to receive and an "answer" modem uses channel B to send and channel A to receive. There is an equivalent Bell Dataset (modem), the Bell 103/113, but this modem uses different FSK frequencies from that of a V.21 modem.

	A Data channels B			
Originate mode	Send channel		Receive channel	
Answer mode	Receive channel		Send channel	
Serial bit	ONE	ZERO	ONE	ZERO
V.21 frequencies	980 Hz	1180 Hz	1650 Hz	1850 Hz
Bell 103 frequencies	1070 Hz	1270 Hz	2025 Hz	2225 Hz

V.23 Recommendation

"600/1200 bit/s modem standardised for use in the general switched telephone network"

A V.23 modem is an asynchronous-only modem which can operate on a

4-wire leased point-to-point or multipoint circuit or a 2-wire leased/switched point-to-point circuit. It was introduced to the UK in the early 'sixties where it was widely used for asynchronous 1200 bit/s multipoint operation.

A V.23 modem uses Frequency Shift Keying and has an optional 75 bit/s reverse channel which gives the modem a 75/1200 bit/s or 1200/75 bit/s full-duplex 2-wire capability. This type of split speed operation was adopted by British Telecom for switched line (PSTN) access to its Prestel Viewdata Service.

The main data channel can operate at either up to 600 bit/s or up to 1200 bit/s. At 600 bit/s the modem frequencies used are 1300 Hz (serial data bit = 0) and 1700 Hz (serial data bit = 1) and at 1200 bit/s they are 1300 Hz (serial data bit = 0) and 2100 Hz (serial data bit = 1). A V.24 interface signal called "data signalling rate selector" (DSRS) is used to select which pair of modem frequencies are used. If DSRS is on (+V) then 1300 Hz and 2100 Hz are used, if DSRS is off (−V) then 1300 Hz and 1700 Hz are used. The reason for frequency switching is to give a V.23 modem the ability to operate at 600 bit/s with switched telephone circuits which have a reduced operational bandwidth.

The nearest USA equivalent modem is the Bell 202 which is not compatible with the V.23 modem frequencies.

Reverse channel		Main data channel		
75 bit/s		600/1200 bit/s	600 bit/s	1200 bit/s
ONE	ZERO	ONE	ZERO	ZERO
390 Hz	450 Hz	1300 Hz	1700 Hz	2100 Hz
Bell Modem 202				
5 bit/s			1800 bit/s	
		ONE		ZERO
387 Hz		1200 Hz		2200 Hz

V.23 provides for the following modem configurations:

4-wire full-duplex point-to-point or half-duplex multipoint leased circuit operation at up to 600 bit/s or 1200 bit/s;

2-wire half-duplex point-to-point leased/switched circuit operation at up to 600 bit/s or 1200 bits/s;

2-wire full-duplex point-to-point leased/switched circuit operation at 75/1200 bit/s or 1200/75 bit/s (75 bit/s in one direction and 1200 bit/s in the other direction — Viewdata compatible).

Modes

1	600 bit/s asynchronous
2	1200 bit/s asynchronous
3	1200/75 bit/s asynchronous
4	75/1200 bit/s asynchronous

V-SERIES RECOMMENDATIONS — ASYNCHRONOUS/ SYNCHRONOUS MODEMS

V.22 Recommendation

"1200 bit/s full-duplex 2-wire modem standardised for use in the general switch-ed telephone network"

A V.22 modem is an asynchronous/synchronous modem which provides 1200 bit/s full-duplex operation over a leased/switched 2-wire circuit and uses fully adaptive automatic equalisation. It performs frequency division multiplexing to create two sub-channels within the bandwidth of a 2-wire line, one is used to send and one is used to receive. This in turn dictates that "originate" and "answer" modes of operation be used. The modulation technique used is 2-level (600 bit/s) or 4-level (1200 bit/s) differential phase shift keying (DPSK) of a 1200 Hz or 2400 Hz carrier. All data is transmitted to line synchronously and asynchronous data is converted by stripping off the start and stop bits before transmission and restoring them after reception. This restricts asynchronous start-stop character formats to 8, 9, 10 or 11 bits per character.

	Data channels	
Originate mode	Send channel	Receive channel
Answer mode	Receive channel	Send channel
Type of modulation	DPSK	DPSK
Centre frequency	1200 Hz	2400 Hz
Guard tone	1800 Hz	

Modes

1	1200 bit/s synchronous
2	1200 bit/s asynchronous
3	600 bit/s synchronous
4	600 bit/s asynchronous
5	0–300 bit/s asynchronous
	1200 bit/s asynchronous

Alternative A   600 or 1200 bit/s synchronous (modes 1, 3)

Alternative B   600 or 1200 bit/s synchronous (modes 1, 3)
or 600 or 1200 bit/s asynchronous (modes 2, 4)

Alternative C   600 or 1200 bit/s synchronous (modes 1, 3)
or 600 or 1200 bit/s asynchronous (modes 2, 4)
or 300 or 1200 bit/s asynchronous (mode 5)

V.22 bis Recommendation

"2400 bit/s full-duplex 2-wire modem standardised for use in the general switch-ed telephone network"

A V.22 bis modem is an asynchronous/synchronous full-duplex 2-wire modem which operates at 2400 bit/s or 1200 bit/s over a 2-wire leased/switched circuit. It uses frequency division multiplexing in a similar way to V.22. When operating at 2400 bit/s it uses quadrature amplitude modulation (QAM) and at 1200 bit/s it is V.22 compatible and uses differential phase shift keying (DPSK).

Modes

1	2400 bit/s synchronous
2	2400 bit/s asynchronous
3	1200 bit/s synchronous (V.22)
4	1200 bit/s asynchronous (V.22)

V.32 Recommendation

The V.32 recommendation covers a family of 2-wire full-duplex asynchronous/synchronous modems for operation at data signalling rates of up to 9600 bit/s for use on the general switched telephone network and on two-wire leased telephone type circuits.

This modem uses echo cancellation techniques instead of frequency division multiplexing to provide full-duplex operation over a 2-wire leased/switched circuit. Quadrature amplitude modulation (QAM) is used.

(At the time of writing this recommendation has not been finalised by CCITT.)

Modes

1	9600 bit/s synchronous
2	9600 bit/s asynchronous
3	4800 bit/s synchronous
4	4800 bit/s asynchronous
5	2400 bit/s synchronous (V.26 ter compatibility)
6	2400 bit/s asynchronous (is under consideration)

V-SERIES RECOMMENDATIONS — SYNCHRONOUS ONLY MODEMS

The manufacturers of synchronous only modems normally design their modems so that a single modem satisfies more than just one V recommendation (e.g. V.27, V.27 bis, V.27 ter.) When these modems are used on the Public Switched Telephone Network (PSTN) the majority provide V.25 auto-answer operation.

V.26 Recommendation

"2400 bit/s modem standardised for use on 4-wire leased telephone type circuits"

A V.26 modem provides full-duplex operation on 4-wire leased point-to-point circuits or half-duplex operation on 4-wire multipoint circuits conforming to Recommendation M.1020. A modem can have an optional full-duplex reverse (supervisory) channel of 75 bit/s full-duplex.

A V.26 modem uses 4-phase differential phase shift keying (DPSK) modulation alternative A or alternative B; the carrier frequency is 1800 Hz.

The modem divides the transmit data serial stream into pairs of consecutive bits (dibits). Each dibit is encoded as a carrier phase change relative to the carrier phase of the immediately preceding dibit.

Dibit	Phase change in degrees	
	Alternative A	Alternative B
00	0	+45
01	+90	+135
11	+180	+225
10	+270	+315

The Bell 201 B/C modem uses DPSK modulation alternative B and is compatible with a V.26 modem (alternative B).

V.26 bis Recommendation

"2400/1200 bit/s modem standardised for use in the general switched telephone network"

A V.26 bis modem provides half-duplex operation on a 2-wire circuit at 2400 bit/s or at a reduced transmission rate of 1200 bit/s. A 75 bit/s full-duplex reverse channel is optional. V.26 4-phase DPSK alternative B modulation is used at 2400 bit/s and 2-phase DPSK modulation at 1200 bit/s.

V.26 ter Recommendation

"2400 bit/s synchronous modem using the echo cancellation technique standardised for use on the general switched telephone network and on point-to-point 2-wire leased telephone type circuits" (At the time of writing this recommendation has not been finalised by CCITT)

V.27 Recommendation

"4800 bit/s modem with manual equaliser standardised for use on leased telephone type circuits"

The principal characteristics of a V.27 modem are:

Capable of full-duplex or half-duplex operation;

Optional full-duplex 75 bit/s reverse channel;

A manually adjustable equaliser is used;

Modulation is 8-phase DPSK of a 1800 Hz carrier (transmit serial data stream is divided into tribits (3 bits) for modulation).

V.27 bis Recommendation

"4800 bit/s modem with automatic equaliser standardised for use on leased telephone type circuits"

The principal characteristics of a V.27 bis modem are:

Operates at 4800 bit/s or 2400 bit/s in full-duplex or half-duplex mode over 4-wire leased circuits or in half-duplex mode over 2-wire leased circuits;

Optional full-duplex 75 bit/s reverse channel;

An automatic adaptive equaliser is used with two start-up sequences one for M.1020 lines and one for lower grade lines;

Incorporates a scrambler/descrambler;

Modulation at 4800 bit/s is per V.27 8-phase DPSK and at 2400 bit/s it is per V.26 4-phase DPSK Alternative A.

V.27 ter Recommendation

"4800/2400 bit/s modem standardised for use in the general switched telephone network"

Provides half-duplex operation over a 2-wire PSTN circuit. Characteristics are similar to V.27 bis but the automatic adaptive equaliser uses more complicated start-up training sequences.

V.29 Recommendation

"9600 bit/s modem standardised for use on leased telephone circuits"

Operates over a full-duplex 4-wire leased circuit (CCITT M.1020 or Bell 3002). Provides fallback (standby) rates of 7200 bit/s and 4800 bit/s. Modem is for leased line operation but some modem manufacturers offer dual dial back-up (full-duplex) over the switched network in case of leased line failure. V.29 recommended time for training is 253 ms (long turn-round time for half-duplex operation).

The modulation method used is Quadrature Amplitude Modulation (QAM) which is a combination of phase and amplitude modulation using eight phases and four amplitudes.

An automatic adaptive equaliser is used to compensate for line distortion.

Provides an optional four port capability (TDM) with ten possible port speed configurations:

	Line speed bit/s	Port speeds in bit/s			
		A	B	C	D
1	9600	9600	—	—	—
2	9600	7200	2400	—	—
3	9600	4800	4800	—	—
4	9600	4800	2400	2400	—
5	9600	2400	2400	2400	2400
6	7200	7200	—	—	—
7	7200	4800	2400	—	—
8	7200	2400	2400	2400	—
9	4800	4800	—	—	—
10	4800	2400	2400	—	—

The port/speed configuration is normally selected by a manual switch on the modem's front panel.

SUMMARY OF V SERIES RECOMMENDATIONS

Asynchronous Only Modems

Up to 1200 bit/s (1800 bit/s − USA)

LINE = 4-WIRE LEASED LINE
V.23   0–600/1200 bit/s FDX (plus 75 bit/s FDX if required)

LINE = 2-WIRE LEASED/SWITCHED LINE
V.21   0–300 bit/s FDX
V.23   0–600/1200 bit/s HDX or 75/1200 bit/s FDX

Asynchronous/Synchronous Modems

1200, 2400, 4800, 9600 bit/s

LINE = 2-WIRE LEASED/SWITCHED LINE
V.22   0–300 bit/s asynchronous FDX
               600 or 1200 bit/s asynchronous/synchronous FDX
V.22 bis   2400 bit/s asynchronous/synchronous FDX
V.26 ter   2400 bit/s asynchronous/synchronous FDX
V.32   9600/4800 bit/s asynchronous/synchronous FDX

Synchronous Only Modems

2400, 4800, 7200, 9600, 12,000, 14,400, 16,000, 16,800, 19,200 bit/s

LINE = 4-WIRE LEASED LINE
V.26   2400 bit/s FDX
V.27   4800 bit/s FDX
V.27 bis   4800 bit/s FDX
V.29   9600/7200/4800 bit/s FDX

LINE = 2-WIRE LEASED/SWITCHED (Single PSTN Dial-up)
V.26 bis   2400/1200 bit/s HDX
V.27 ter   4800/2400 bit/s HDX
V.29   9600/7200/4800 bit/s HDX (253 msec)

LINE = 4-WIRE SWITCHED (Double PSTN Dial-up)
V.29   9600/7200/4800 bit/s FDX

Wide-Band Synchronous Only Modems

48 kbit/s to 168 kbit/s

LINE = WIDE-BAND CIRCUIT
V.35   48 kbits FDX
V.36   48–72 kbit/s FDX
V.37   96–168 kbit/s FDX

V.54 Recommendation

"Loop test devices for modems"

This recommendation defines four loop tests for DTE (Computer/Terminal) and DCE (modem) as shown in Fig. A.1.

Loop 1 is used as a basic test on the operation of a DTE, signals sent by the DTE are returned directly to the same DTE for checking. The loop should be set up inside the DTE as close as possible to the interface.

Loop 2 is a loop placed on the DTE side of the distant DCE, it is formed by applying predetermined conditions to the interchange circuits at logic voltage levels within the DCE (Remote Digital Loopback). It is designed to test the line and the distant DCE but can be used only with a full-duplex DCE.

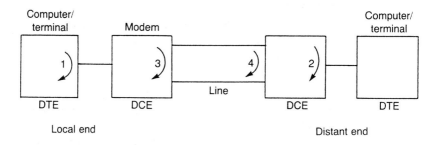

Fig. A.1. Loop tests 1-4.

Loop 3 is a loop placed across the transmit and receive paths on the analogue line side of the Local DCE (Local Analogue Loopback).

Loop 4 applies only to 4-wire lines and is formed by looping the transmit and receive paths at the distant end through a suitable attenuator.

Modem interchange circuits are used to place a modem in loopback and to determine that the modem is in test mode.

Interchange circuit 140 (Pin 21) is defined as "remote loopback for point-to-point circuits" and is used by a DTE to initiate a V.54 Loop 2.

Interchange circuit 141 (Pin 18) is defined as "local loopback" and is used by a DTE to initiate a V.54 Loop 3.

Interchange circuit 142 (Pin 25) is defined as "test indicator" and informs a DTE that its modem is in test mode.

Appendix B

CCITT X-SERIES RECOMMENDATIONS

The following is a list of CCITT X-Series recommendations which apply to public data networks.

X.1	International user classes of service in public data networks and ISDNs.
X.2	International data transmission services and optional user facilities in public data neworks
X.3	Packet assembly/disassembly facility (PAD) in a public data network
X.4	General structure of signals of International Alphabet No. 5 code for data transmission over public data networks
X.15	Definitions of terms concerning public data networks
X.20	Interface between data terminal equipment (DTE) and data circuit-terminating equipment (DCE) for start-stop transmission services on public data networks
X.20 bis	Use on public data networks of data terminal equipment (DTE) which is designed for interfacing to asynchronous duplex V-Series modems
X.21	Interface between data terminal equipment (DTE) and data circuit-terminating equipment (DCE) for synchronous operation on public data networks
X.21 bis	Use on public data networks of data terminal equipment (DTE) which is designed for interfacing to synchronous V-Series modems
X.22	Multiplex DTE/DCE interface for user classes 3–6
X.24	List of definitions for interchange circuits between data terminal equipment (DTE) and data circuit-terminating equipment (DCE) on public data networks
X.25	Interface between data terminal equipment (DTE) and data circuit-terminating equipment (DCE) for terminals operating in the packet mode and connected to public data networks by dedicated circuit
X.26	Electrical characteristics for unbalanced double-current interchange circuits for general use with integrated circuit equipment in the field of data communications
X.27	Electrical characteristics for balanced double-current interchange circuits for general use with integrated circuit equipment in the field of data communications

X.28   DTE/DCE interface for a start-stop mode data terminal equipment accessing the packet assembly/disassembly facility (PAD) in a public data network situated in the same country

X.29   Procedures for the exchange of control information and user data between a packet assembly/disassembly facility (PAD) and a packet mode DTE or another PAD

X.30   Support of X.21 and X.21 bis based DTEs by an ISDN

X.31   Support of Packet Mode Terminal Equipment by an ISDN

X.32   Interface between data terminal equipment (DTE) and data circuit terminating equipment (DCE) for terminals operating in the packet mode and accessing a packet switched public data network through a public switched network

X.50   Fundamental parameters of a multiplexing scheme for the international interface between synchronous data networks

X.50 bis   Fundamental parameters of a 48 kbit/s user data signalling rate transmission scheme for the international interface between synchronous data networks

X.51   Fundamental parameters of a multiplexing scheme for the international interface between synchronous data networks using 10-bit envelope structure

X.51 bis   Fundamental parameters of a 48 kbit/s user data signalling rate transmission scheme for the international interface between synchronous data networks using 10-bit envelope structure

X.60   Common channel signalling for circuit switched data applications

X.61   Signalling System No. 7 — Data user part

X.70   Terminal and transit control signalling for start-stop services on international circuits between anisochronous data networks

X.71   Decentralised terminal and transit control signalling system on international circuits between synchronous data networks

X.75   Terminal and transit call control procedures and data transfer system on international circuits between packet-switched data networks

X.80   Interworking of inter-exchange signalling systems for circuit switched data services

X.87   Principles and procedures for realisation of international user facilities and network utilities in public data networks

X.92   Hypothetical reference connections for public synchronous data networks

X.96   Call progress signals in public data networks

X.110   Routing principles for international public data services through switched public data networks of the same type

X.121   International numbering plan for public data networks

X.130   Provisional objectives for call set-up and clear-down times in public synchronous data networks (circuit switching)

X.132   Provisional objectives for grade of service in international data communications over circuit switched public data networks

X.150   DTE and DCE test loops for public data networks

X.180   Administrative arrangements for international closed user groups (CUGs)

X.244   Procedure for the exchange of protocol identification during virtual call establishment on packet switched public data networks

Appendix C

LIST OF PACKET SWITCHED DATA NETWORKS

The following countries have implemented a packet switched data network:

COUNTRY	NETWORK NAME
Argentina	ARPAC
Australia	AUSTPAC
	MIDAS
Austria	DATEX-P
	RADIO AUSTRIA
Bahrain	IDAS
Belgium	DCS
Brazil	INTERDATA
Canada	DATAPAC
	GLOBEDAT-P
	INFOSWITCH
Chile	?
Denmark	DATAPAK
Eire	EIRPAC
Finland	FINNPAK (DATAPAK)
France	TRANSPAC
	NTI
French Guiana	DOMPAC
French Polynesia	TOMPAC
Gabon	GABOPAC
Germany	DATEX P
Greece	HELPAC
Guadeloupe	DOMPAC
Hong Kong	IDAS (INTELPAK)
	PSDS (DATAPAK)
Israel	ISRANET
Italy	ITAPAC
Ivory Coast	SYTRANPAC
Japan	DDX-P
	VENUS-P
	ICAS
Luxembourg	LUXPAC
Martinique	DOMPAC
Mexico	TELPAC

COUNTRY	NETWORK NAME
Netherlands	DABAS
	DATANET 1
New Zealand	PACNET
Norway	NORPAK (DATAPAK)
Peru	?
Philippines	PHILCOM
	GMCR
Portugal	TELEPAC
Singapore	TELEPAC
South Africa	SAPONET-P
South Korea	DACOM-NET
Spain	TIDA
	IBERPAC
Sweden	TELEPAK (DATAPAK)
Switzerland	TELEPAC
Taiwan	UDAS
Thailand	IDAR
Trinidad	TEXTEL
United Kingdom	PSS
	IPSS
United States	ADP-AUTONET
of America	COMPUSERVE
	DATAPAK (TRT)
	DBS (WUI)
	FTCC
	LSDS (RCA)
	MARKNET
	TELENET
	TYMNET
	UDTS (ITT)
	UNINET
	WUTCO
Venezuela	?
Yugoslavia	?

Appendix D

CCITT I-SERIES RECOMMENDATIONS FOR ISDN

The I. numbers and titles of the Integrated Services Digital Network (ISDN) draft recommendations in the following list are liable to change.

I.110   General structure of the I-Series Recommendations

I.111   Relationship with other recommendations relevant to ISDNs

I.112   Vocabulary of terms for ISDNs

I.120   ISDN concept

I.210   Principles of telecommunication services supported by an ISDN

I.211   Bearer services supported by an ISDN

I.212   Tele-services supported by an ISDN

I.300   ISDN functional principles

I.310   Network functional principles

I.320   ISDN protocol reference model

I.32X   ISDN functional architectural model

I.325   ISDN connection types

I.330   ISDN numbering and addressing principles

I.340   ISDN connection types

I.410   General aspects and principles relating to recommendations on ISDN user-network interfaces

I.411   ISDN user-network interfaces — reference configurations

I.412   ISDN user-network interfaces — interface structures and access capabilities.

I.420   Basic user-network interface

I.421   Primary rate user-network interface

I.440   Specification of the ISDN user-network interface data link layer protocol

I.450   General aspects of the ISDN user-network interface layer 3 functions and protocols

I.451   Specification of the ISDN user-network interface layer 3 protocol

I.461   Support of X.21 and X.21 bis based DTEs by an ISDN (X.30)

I.462   Support of packet mode terminal equipments by an ISDN (X.31)

216

Appendix E

OPEN SYSTEMS INTERCONNECTION (OSI)

The International Organisation for Standardisation (ISO) is responsible for the development of the OSI standards.

Open Systems Interconnection (OSI) is a a concept in which the relationship between a network and the services which it can support are shown by a hierarchy of protocol layers. Each layer contains one or more functions contained between an upper and lower logical boundary. Each layer uses the services of the lower layers in conjunction with its own functions to create new services which are made available to the higher layers.

The following is a brief summary of the seven layers of the model.

LAYER 1
Physical layer includes transmission of signals

LAYER 2
Data link layer includes synchronisation and some control over the influence of error with the physical layer.

LAYER 3
Network layer includes routing and switching functions.

LAYER 4
Transport layer uses layer 1 to 3 to provide an end to end service to the higher layer functions.

LAYER 5
Session layer controls the establishment and termination of transport connections.

LAYER 6
Presentation layer includes data formatting and code conversion.

LAYER 7
Application layer includes user programs.

In the UK the Department of Trade and Industry (DTI) "Focus" committee on Information Technology Standards have recommended the "Intercept Strategy" for Open Systems Interconnection (OSI). The aims of this strategy are to identify and promote OSI Standards which are close to, but have not yet reached, final international agreement. This is to encourage UK suppliers and users of text and data processing equipment to implement OSI Standards without waiting for the full process of international standardisation to be complete. The "Intercept" stategy is the responsibility of the DTI's Information Technology Standards Unit which is producing Technical Guides (TGs) under the general heading of FOCUS: Standards for IT. The following are examples:

218

TG 100/1   Intercept recommendations for the OSI Network Layer

TG 100/2   Intercept recommendations for provision of OSI Network Service over X.25

TG 101/1   Intercept recommendations for Local Area Networks according to Logical Link Control

TG 101/2   Intercept recommendations for Local Area Networks according to the CSMA/CD Access Method

TG 101/4   Intercept recommendations for Local Area Networks according to Token Passing Ring Access Method

TG 101/5   Introduction to Local Area Networks

TG 102/1   Intercept recommendations for the OSI Transport Layer

TG 103/1   Intercept recommendations for the OSI Session Layer.

Appendix F

STANDARDS ORGANISATIONS

ANSI   American National Standards Institute

BSI   British Standards Institute

BT   British Telecom

CCITT International Telegraph and Telephone Consultative Committee

ECMA European Computer Manufacturers Assocation

EIA   Electronics Industries Association

IEEE   Institute of Electrical and Electronics Engineers

ISO   International Organisation for Standardisation

ITU   International Telecommunication Union

JNT   Joint Network Team of the Computer Board and Research Councils

Appendix G

Appendix H

DAA	Data Access Arrangement
DASS	Digital Access Signalling System
DBU	Dial Back-up Unit
DCE	Data Circuit-Terminating Equipment
DCE1A	Data Control Equipment No 1A (BT)
DCPBX	Digitally Connected Private Branch Exchange
DDCMP	Digital Data Communications Message Protocol
DDD	Direct Distance Dial
DDS	Dataphone Digital Services (AT&T)
DEC	Digital Equipment Corporation
DEL	Direct Exchange Line
DIP	Dual In-line Package
DIX	Digital Equipment Corporation / Intel / Xerox
DLE	Data Link Escape
DNIC	Data Network Identification Code
DOVE	Data Over Voice Equipment
DPNSS	Digital Private Network Signalling System
DPSK	Differential Phase Shift Keying
DSAP	Destination Service Access Point (L-PDU)
DSR	Data Set Ready
DSRS	Data Signalling Rate Selector
DTE	Data Terminal Equipment
DTI	Department of Trade and Industry
DTR	Data Terminal Ready
EBCDIC	Extended Binary Coded Decimal Interchange Code
ECMA	European Computer Manufacturers Assocation
EIA	Electronics Industries Assocation
EM	End of Media
ENQ	Enquiry
EON	End Of Number
ETB	End of Transmission Block
ETX	End of Transmission
FAX	Facsimile
FCS	Frame Checking (Check) Sequence
FDDI	Fibre Distributed Data Interface
FDM	Frequency Division Multiplexer (Modulation)
FDX	Full-Duplex
FEC	Forward Error Correction
FEP	Front End Processor
FIFO	First In First Out
FSK	Frequency Shift Keying
GHz	Gigahertz
GS	Group Separator
HDLC	High Level Data Link Control
HDX	Half-Duplex
HT	Horizontal Tab
Hz	Hertz (cycles per second)
IA5	International Alphabet No. 5 (ASCII)
IBM	International Business Machines Corporation

ICL	International Computers Ltd
IDA	Integrated Digital Access
IDN	Integrated Digital Network
IEEE	Institute of Electrical and Electronic Engineers
in.	Inches
ISDN	Integrated Services Digital Network
ISO	International Organisation for Standardisation
ISPBX	Integrated Services Private Branch Exchange
ITA2	International Telegraph Alphabet No 2 (Baudot)
ITU	International Telecommunications Union
JNT	Joint Network Team (Computer Board and Research Councils)
Kbit/s	Kilobits per second
KHz	Kilohertz
km	Kilometres
L-PDU	Logical Link Control - Protocol Data Unit (IEEE 802.2)
LAN	Local Area Network
LAP	Link Access Procedure
LAPB	Link Acess Procedure Balanced
LDDI	Local Distributed Data Interface
LLC	Logical Link Control
LRC	Longitudinal Redundancy Check
LSI	Large Scale Integration
LT	Line Termination
LTE	Line Terminating Equipment
m	Metres
mA	Milliamps
MAC	Media Access Control
MAU	Medium Attachment Unit
Mbit/s	Megabits per second
MDF	Master Distribution Frame
mm	Millimetres
ms	Milliseconds
NAK	Negative Acknowledge
Nr	Receive Sequence Count
NRM	Normal Response Mode
Ns	Send Sequence Count
NT	Network Termination
NTE	Network Termination Equipment
NTU	Network Termination Unit
NUA	Network User Address
NUI	Network User Identity
OSI	Open Systems Interconnection
PABX	Private Automatic (Automated) Branch Exchange
PAD	Packet Assembler/Disassembler
PBX	Private Branch Exchange
PCB	Printed Circuit Board
PCM	Pulse Code Modulation
PDC	Permanent Datacall (PSS)
pF	Picofarads

POS	Point Of Sale
PSDN	Packet Switched Data Network
PSE	Packet Switching Exchange
PSPDN	Packet Switched Public Data Network
PSS	Packet SwitchStream (BT)
PSTN	Public Switched Telephone Network
PTT	Postal Telegraph And Telephone agencies
PVC	Permanent Virtual Circuit (X.25)
QAM	Quadrature Amplitude Modulation
REJ	Reject
RF	Radio Frequency
RFS	Ready For Sending
RI	Ringing Indicator
RJE	Remote Job Entry
RNR	Receive Not Ready
RR	Receive Ready
RS	Recommended Standard (EIA)
RSET	Receive Signal Element Timing
RTS	Request To Send
RVI	Reverse Interrupt
SCVF	Single Channel Voice Frequency
SDLC	Synchronous Data Link Control (IBM)
SH	Short Haul
SNA	System Network Architecture (IBM)
SOH	Start Of Heading
SREJ	Selective Reject
SSAP	Source Service Access Point (L-PDU)
STX	Start Of Text
SVC	Switched Virtual Circuit (X.25)
SYN	Synchronous Idle
S+DX	Speech Plus Duplex
TA	Terminal Adapter
TAN	Trunk Access Node
TDM	Time Division Multiplexer
TDMA	Time Division Multiple Access
TE	Terminal Equipment
TSET	Transmit Signal Element Timing
US	Unit Separator
USA	United States of America
USASCII	USA Standard Code for Information Interchange
VDT	Visual Display Terminal
VDU	Visual Display Unit
VRC	Vertical Redundancy Check
WACK	Wait Before Transmit Positive Acknowledge
WAL2	Walsh 2

Appendix I

CODE TABLES
CCITT IA5 AND IBM EBCDIC

The CCITT International Alphabet No. 5 (IA5) described in CCITT Recommendation V.3. and the IBM Extended Binary Coded Decimal Interchange Code (EBCDIC) are shown in the following tables.

There are many versions of alphabets and codes provided for different countries and communications products. The International version of IA5 and the IBM 2780/3780 version of EBCDIC are shown.

The four hexadecimal values shown for each character in the IA5 table include the parity bit when it is a permanent "0", a permanent "1", used for odd parity and used for even parity.

						COLUMN							
					b_7	0	0	0	0	1	1	1	1
					b_6	0	0	1	1	0	0	1	1
					b_5	0	1	0	1	0	1	0	1
b_4	b_3	b_2	b_1	HEX	DEC	0	1	2	3	4	5	6	7
0	0	0	0	0	0	NUL	TC_7 (DLE)	SP	0	@	P	`	p
0	0	0	1	1	1	TC_1 (SOH)	DC_1	!	1	A	Q	a	q
0	0	1	0	2	2	TC_2 (STX)	DC_2	"	2	B	R	b	r
0	0	1	1	3	3	TC_3 (ETX)	DC_3	# (£)	3	C	S	c	s
0	1	0	0	4	4	TC_4 (EOT)	DC_4	¤ ($)	4	D	T	d	t
0	1	0	1	5	5	TC_5 (ENQ)	TC_8 (NAK)	%	5	E	U	e	u
0	1	1	0	6	6	TC_6 (ACK)	TC_9 (SYN)	&	6	F	V	f	v
0	1	1	1	7	7	BEL	TC_{10} (ETB)	'	7	G	W	g	w
1	0	0	0	8	8	FE_0 (BS)	CAN	(	8	H	X	h	x
1	0	0	1	9	9	FE_1 (HT)	EM	)	9	I	Y	i	y
1	0	1	0	A	10	FE_2 (LF)	SUB	*	:	J	Z	j	z
1	0	1	1	B	11	FE_3 (VT)	ESC	+	;	K	[	k	{
1	1	0	0	C	12	FE_4 (FF)	IS_4 (FS)	,	<	L	/	l	¦
1	1	0	1	D	13	FE_5 (CR)	IS_3 (GS)	−	=	M	]	m	}
1	1	1	0	E	14	SO	IS_2 (RS)	.	>	N	^	n	‾
1	1	1	1	F	15	SI	IS_1 (US)	/	?	O	_	o	DEL

ROW

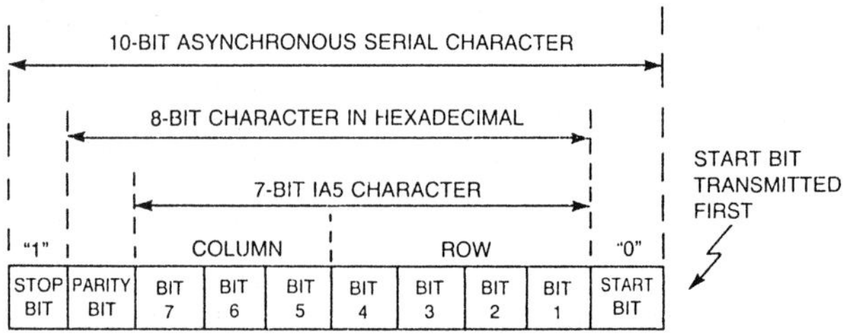

Fig. I-1. 7-Bit International Alphabet No. 5 (IA5).

Column and row position	Hexadecimal code IA No. 5 plus parity				Character	Description
	"0"	"1"	ODD	EVEN		
0/0	00	80	80	00	NUL	NULL
0/1	01	81	01	81	SOH	START OF HEADING
0/2	02	82	02	82	STX	START OF TEXT
0/3	03	83	83	03	ETX	END OF TEXT
0/4	04	84	04	84	EOT	END OF TRANSMISSION
0/5	05	85	85	05	ENQ	ENQUIRY
0/6	06	86	86	06	ACK	ACKNOWLEDGE
0/7	07	87	07	87	BEL	BELL
0/8	08	88	08	88	BS	BACKSPACE
0/9	09	89	89	09	HT	HORIZONTAL TABULATION
0/10	0A	8A	8A	0A	LF	LINE FEED
0/11	0B	8B	0B	8B	VT	VERTICAL TABULATION
0/12	0C	8C	8C	0C	FF	FORM FEED
0/13	0D	8D	0D	8D	CR	CARRIAGE RETURN
0/14	0E	8E	0E	8E	SO	SHIFT-OUT
0/15	0F	8F	8F	0F	SI	SHIFT-IN
1/0	10	90	10	90	DLE	DATA LINK ESCAPE
1/1	11	91	91	11	DC1	DEVICE CONTROL 1
1/2	12	92	92	12	DC2	DEVICE CONTROL 2
1/3	13	93	13	93	DC3	DEVICE CONTROL 3
1/4	14	94	94	14	DC4	DEVICE CONTROL 4
1/5	15	95	15	95	NAK	NEGATIVE ACKNOWLEDGE
1/6	16	96	16	96	SYN	SYNCHRONOUS IDLE
1/7	17	97	97	17	ETB	END OF TRANSMISSION BLOCK
1/8	18	98	98	18	CAN	CANCEL
1/9	19	99	19	99	EM	END OF MEDIUM
1/10	1A	9A	1A	9A	SUB	SUBSTITUTE CHARACTER
1/11	1B	9B	9B	1B	ESC	ESCAPE
1/12	1C	9C	1C	9C	FS	FILE SEPARATOR
1/13	1D	9D	9D	1D	GS	GROUP SEPARATOR
1/14	1E	9E	9E	1E	RS	RECORD SEPARATOR
1/15	1F	9F	IF	9F	US	UNIT SEPARATOR
2/0	20	A0	20	A0	SP	SPACE
2/1	21	A1	A1	21	!	EXCLAMATION MARK
2/2	22	A2	A2	22	"	QUOTATION MARK, DIAERESIS
2/3	23	A3	23	A3	£	POUND OR NUMBER SIGN
2/4	24	A4	A4	24	$	DOLLAR OR CURRENCY SIGN
2/5	25	A5	25	A5	%	PERCENT SIGN
2/6	26	A6	26	A6	&	AMPERSAND
2/7	27	A7	A7	27	`	APOSTROPHE, ACUTE ANGLE
2/8	28	A8	A8	28	(	LEFT ROUND BRACKET
2/9	29	A9	29	A9	)	RIGHT ROUND BRACKET
2/10	2A	AA	2A	AA	*	ASTERISK
2/11	2B	AB	AB	2B	+	PLUS SIGN
2/12	2C	AC	2C	AC	,	COMMA, CEDILLA
2/13	2D	AD	AD	2D	−	HYPHEN, MINUS SIGN
2/14	2E	AE	AE	2E	.	FULL STOP (PERIOD)
2/15	2F	AF	2F	AF	/	SOLIDUS

Column and row position	Hexadecimal code IA No. 5 plus parity				Character	Description
	"0"	"1"	ODD	EVEN		
3/0	30	B0	B0	30	0	FIGURES
3/1	31	B1	31	B1	1	
3/2	32	B2	32	B2	2	
3/3	33	B3	B3	33	3	
3/4	34	B4	34	B4	4	
3/5	35	B5	B5	35	5	
3/6	36	B6	B6	36	6	
3/7	37	B7	37	B7	7	
3/8	38	B8	38	B8	8	
3/9	39	B9	B9	39	9	
3/10	3A	BA	BA	3A	:	COLON
3/11	3B	BB	3B	BB	;	SEMI-COLON
3/12	3C	BC	BC	3C	<	LESS-THAN SIGN
3/13	3D	BD	3D	BD	=	EQUALS SIGN
3/14	3E	BE	3E	BE	>	GREATER-THAN SIGN
3/15	3F	BF	BF	3F	?	QUESTION MARK
4/0	40	C0	40	C0	@	COMMERCIAL AT
4/1	41	C1	C1	41	A	UPPER CASE LETTERS
4/2	42	C2	C2	42	B	
4/3	43	C3	43	C3	C	
4/4	44	C4	C4	44	D	
4/5	45	C5	45	C5	E	
4/6	46	C6	46	C6	F	
4/7	47	C7	C7	47	G	
4/8	48	C8	C8	48	H	
4/9	49	C9	49	C9	I	
4/10	4A	CA	4A	CA	J	
4/11	4B	CB	CB	4B	K	
4/12	4C	CC	4C	CC	L	
4/13	4D	CD	CD	4D	M	
4/14	4E	CE	CE	4E	N	
4/15	4F	CF	4F	CF	O	
5/0	50	D0	D0	50	P	
5/1	51	D1	51	D1	Q	
5/2	52	D2	52	D2	R	
5/3	53	D3	D3	53	S	
5/4	54	D4	54	D4	T	
5/5	55	D5	D5	55	U	
5/6	56	D6	D6	56	V	
5/7	57	D7	57	D7	W	
5/8	58	D8	58	D8	X	
5/9	59	D9	D9	59	Y	
5/10	5A	DA	DA	5A	Z	
5/11	5B	DB	5B	DB	[	LEFT SQUARE BRACKET
5/12	5C	DC	DC	5C	\	REVERSE SOLIDUS
5/13	5D	DD	5D	DD	]	RIGHT SQUARE BRACKET
5/14	5E	DE	5E	DE	^	UPWARD ARROW HEAD, CIRCUMFLEX ACCENT
5/15	5F	DF	DF	5F	_	UNDERLINE

Column and row position	Hexadecimal code				Character	Description
	IA No. 5 plus parity					
	"0"	"1"	ODD	EVEN		
6/0	60	E0	E0	60	`	GRAVE ACCENT
6/1	61	E1	61	E1	a	LOWER CASE LETTERS
6/2	62	E2	62	E2	b	
6/3	63	E3	E3	63	c	
6/4	64	E4	64	E4	d	
6/5	65	E5	E5	65	e	
6/6	66	E6	E6	66	f	
6/7	67	E7	67	E7	g	
6/8	68	E8	68	E8	h	
6/9	69	E9	E9	69	i	
6/10	6A	EA	EA	6A	j	
6/11	6B	EB	6B	EB	k	
6/12	6C	EC	EC	6C	l	
6/13	6D	ED	6D	ED	m	
6/14	6E	EE	6E	EE	n	
6/15	6F	EF	EF	6F	o	
7/0	70	F0	70	F0	p	
7/1	71	F1	F1	71	q	
7/2	72	F2	F2	72	r	
7/3	73	F3	73	F3	s	
7/4	74	F4	F4	74	t	
7/5	75	F5	75	F5	u	
7/6	76	F6	76	F6	v	
7/7	77	F7	F7	77	w	
7/8	78	F8	F8	78	x	
7/9	79	F9	79	F9	y	
7/10	7A	FA	7A	FA	z	
7/11	7B	FB	FB	7B	{	LEFT CURLY BRACKET
7/12	7C	FC	7C	FC	|	VERTICAL LINE
7/13	7D	FD	FD	7C	}	RIGHT CURLY BRACKET
7/14	7E	FE	FE	7E	‾	OVERLINE, TILDE
7/15	7F	FF	7F	FF	DEL	DELETE

Appendix I

		COLUMN															
HEX		0	1	2	3	4	5	6	7	8	9	A	B	C	D	E	F
	DEC	0	1	2	3	4	5	6	7	8	9	10	11	12	13	14	15
0	0	NUL	DLE	DS		SP	&	-						{	}	\	0
1	1	SOH	DCI	SOS				/		a	j	~		A	J		1
2	2	STX	DC2	FS	SYN					b	k	s		B	K	S	2
3	3	ETX	DC3							c	l	t		C	L	T	3
4	4	PF	RES	BYP	PN					d	m	u		D	M	U	4
5	5	HT	NL	LF	RS					e	n	v		E	N	V	5
6	6	LC	BS	ETB	UC					f	o	w		F	O	W	6
7	7	DEL	IL	ESC	EOT					g	p	x		G	P	X	7
8	8	GE	CAN							h	q	y		H	Q	Y	8
9	9	RLF	EM						/	i	r	z		I	R	Z	9
A	10	SMM	CC	SM		¢	!	|	:								LVM
B	11	VT	CU1	CU2	CU3	.	$	,	#								
C	12	FF	IFS		DC4	<	.	%	@					⌐		⊣	
D	13	CR	IGS	ENQ	NAK	(	)	_	'								
E	14	SO	IRS	ACK		+	;	>	=					⊔			
F	15	SI	IUS	BEL	SUB	|	¬	?	"								EO

(Left margin label: R O W)

Fig. I-2. 8-Bit Extended Binary Coded Decimal Interchange Code (EBCDIC).

Column and row position	Hexadecimal code EBCDIC	Character	Description
0/0	00	NUL	NULL
0/1	01	SOH	START OF HEADING
0/2	02	STX	START OF TEXT
0/3	03	ETX	END OF TEXT
0/4	04	PF	PUNCH OFF
0/5	05	HT	HORIZONTAL TABULATION
0/6	06	LC	LOWER CASE
0/7	07	DEL	DELETE
0/8	08	GE	GRAPHIC ESCAPE
0/9	09	RLF	REVERSE LINE FEED
0/10	0A	SMM	START OF MANUAL MESSAGE
0/11	0B	VT	VERTICAL TABULATION
0/12	0C	FF	FORM FEED
0/13	0D	CR	CARRIAGE RETURN
0/14	0E	SO	SHIFT-OUT
0/15	0F	SI	SHIFT-IN
1/0	10	DLE	DATA LINK ESCAPE
1/1	11	DC1	DEVICE CONTROL 1
1/2	12	DC2	DEVICE CONTROL 2
1/3	13	DC3	DEVICE CONTROL 3
1/4	14	RES	RESTORE
1/5	15	NL	NEW LINE
1/6	16	BS	BACKSPACE
1/7	17	IL	IDLE
1/8	18	CAN	CANCEL
1/9	19	EM	END OF MEDIUM
1/10	1A	CC	CURSOR CONTROL
1/11	1B	CU1	CUSTOMER USE 1
1/12	1C	IFS	INTERCHANGE FILE SEPARATOR
1/13	1D	IGS	INTERCHANGE GROUP SEPARATOR
1/14	1E	IRS	INTERCHANGE RECORD SEPARATOR
1/15	1F	IUS	INTERCHANGE UNIT SEPARATOR
2/0	20	DS	DIGIT SELECT
2/1	21	SOS	START OF SIGNIFICANCE
2/2	22	FS	FIELD SEPARATOR
2/3	23		
2/4	24	BYP	BYPASS
2/5	25	LF	LINE FEED
2/6	26	ETB	END OF TRANSMISSION BLOCK
2/7	27	ESC	ESCAPE
2/8	28		
2/9	29		
2/10	2A	SM	SET MODE
2/11	2B	CU2	CUSTOMER USE 2
2/12	2C		
2/13	2D	ENQ	ENQUIRY
2/14	2E	ACK	ACKNOWLEDGE
2/15	2F	BEL	BELL

Column and row position	Hexadecimal code EBCDIC	Character	Description
3/0	30		
3/1	31		
3/2	32	SYN	SYNCHRONOUS IDLE
3/3	33		
3/4	34	PN	PUNCH ON
3/5	35	RS	READER STOP
3/6	36	UC	UPPER CASE
3/7	37	EOT	END OF TRANSMISSION
3/8	38		
3/9	39		
3/10	3A		
3/11	3B	CU3	CUSTOMER USE 3
3/12	3C	DC4	DEVICE CONTROL 4
3/13	3D	NAK	NEGATIVE ACKNOWLEDGE
3/14	3E		
3/15	3F	SUB	SUBSTITUTE CHARACTER
4/0	40	SP	SPACE
4/1	41		
4/2	42		
4/3	43		
4/4	44		
4/5	45		
4/6	46		
4/7	47		
4/8	48		
4/9	49		
4/10	4A	¢	CENT SIGN
4/11	4B	.	FULL STOP
4/12	4C	<	LESS-THAN SIGN
4/13	4D	(	LEFT ROUND BRACKET
4/14	4E	+	PLUS SIGN
4/15	4F			LOGICAL OR
5/0	50	&	AMPERSAND
5/1	51		
5/2	52		
5/3	53		
5/4	54		
5/5	55		
5/6	56		
5/7	57		
5/8	58		
5/9	59		
5/10	5A	!	EXCLAMATION MARK
5/11	5B	$	DOLLAR SIGN
5/12	5C	*	ASTERISK
5/13	5D	)	RIGHT ROUND BRACKET
5/14	5E	;	SEMI-COLON
5/15	5F	¬	LOGICAL NOT

Column and row position	Hexadecimal code EBCDIC	Character	Description
6/0	60	–	HYPHEN, MINUS SIGN
6/1	61	/	SOLIDUS (SLASH)
6/2	62		
6/3	63		
6/4	64		
6/5	65		
6/6	66		
6/7	67		
6/8	68		
6/9	69		
6/10	6A	|	VERTICAL LINE
6/11	6B	,	COMMA, CEDILLA
6/12	6C	%	PERCENT SIGN
6/13	6D	_	UNDERLINE
6/14	6E	>	GREATER-THAN SIGN
6/15	6F	?	QUESTION MARK
7/0	70		
7/1	71		
7/2	72		
7/3	73		
7/4	74		
7/5	75		
7/6	76		
7/7	77		
7/8	78		
7/9	79	`	GRAVE ACCENT
7/10	7A	:	COLON
7/11	7B	£	NUMBER SIGN
7/12	7C	@	COMMERCIAL AT
7/13	7D	'	APOSTROPHE
7/14	7E	=	EQUALS SIGN
7/15	7F	"	QUOTATION MARK
8/0	80		
8/1	81	a	
8/2	82	b	
8/3	83	c	
8/4	84	d	
8/5	85	e	
8/6	86	f	
8/7	87	g	
8/8	88	h	
8/9	89	i	
8/10	8A		
8/11	8B		
8/12	8C		
8/13	8D		
8/14	8E		
8/15	8F		

Column and row position	Hexadecimal code EBCDIC	Character	Description
9/0	90		
9/1	91	j	
9/2	92	k	
9/3	93	l	
9/4	94	m	
9/5	95	n	
9/6	96	o	
9/7	97	p	
9/8	98	q	
9/9	99	r	
9/10	9A		
9/11	9B		
9/12	9C		
9/13	9D		
9/14	9E		
9/15	9F		
10/0	A0		
10/1	A1	~	TILDE
10/2	A2	s	
10/3	A3	t	
10/4	A4	u	
10/5	A5	v	
10/6	A6	w	
10/7	A7	x	
10/8	A8	y	
10/9	A9	z	
10/10	AA		
10/11	AB		
10/12	AC		
10/13	AD		
10/14	AE		
10/15	AF		
11/0	B0		
11/1	B1		
11/2	B2		
11/3	B3		
11/4	B4		
11/5	B5		
11/6	B6		
11/7	B7		
11/8	B8		
11/9	B9		
11/10	BA		
11/11	BB		
11/12	BC		
11/13	BD		
11/14	BE		
11/15	BF		

Column and row position	Hexadecimal code EBCDIC	Character	Description
12/0	C0	{	LEFT CURLY BRACKET
12/1	C1	A	
12/2	C2	B	
12/3	C3	C	
12/4	C4	D	
12/5	C5	E	
12/6	C6	F	
12/7	C7	G	
12/8	C8	H	
12/9	C9	I	
12/10	CA		
12/11	CB		
12/12	CC	⌐	HOOK
12/13	CD		
12/14	CE	⊔	FORK
12/15	CF		
13/0	D0	}	RIGHT CURLY BRACKET
13/1	D1	J	
13/2	D2	K	
13/3	D3	L	
13/4	D4	M	
13/5	D5	N	
13/6	D6	O	
13/7	D7	P	
13/8	D8	Q	
13/9	D9	R	
13/10	DA		
13/11	DB		
13/12	DC		
13/13	DD		
13/14	DE		
13/15	DF		
14/0	E0	\	REVERSE SOLIDUS (SLANT)
14/1	E1		
14/2	E2	S	
14/3	E3	T	
14/4	E4	U	
14/5	E5	V	
14/6	E6	W	
14/7	E7	X	
14/8	E8	Y	
14/9	E9	Z	
14/10	EA		
14/11	EB		
14/12	EC	⌐	CHAIR
14/13	ED		
14/14	EE		
14/15	EF		

Appendix I

Column and row position	Hexadecimal code EBCDIC	Character	Description
15/0	F0	0	FIGURES
15/1	F1	1	
15/2	F2	2	
15/3	F3	3	
15/4	F4	4	
15/5	F5	5	
15/6	F6	6	
15/7	F7	7	
15/8	F8	8	
15/9	F9	9	
15/10	FA	LVM	LONG VERTICAL MARK
15/11	FB		
15/12	FC		
15/13	FD		
15/14	FE		
15/15	FF	EO	EIGHT ONES

Index